THE KEN HAWLEY EXPERIENCE

DEREK BATESON

KEN HAWLEY COLLECTION TRUST

KEN HAWLEY COLLECTION TRUST

Published by the Ken Hawley Collection Trust, Kelham Island Museum, Alma Street, Sheffield S3 8RY

Derek Bateson, Author and Commissioning Editor

© Ken Hawley Collection Trust, 2010
Copyright in certain images rests with the photographer(s) as indicated elsewhere

ISBN 978-0-9566806-0-0

Design and Production, Alan Gray, amwgray@gmail.com and Tim Mackey, timmackey48@googlemail.com
Photography Direction, Derek Bateson, derekandbarbara@blueyonder.co.uk
Printed in England by Northend Creative Print Solutions, Clyde Road, Sheffield, S8 0TZ
Tel: 0114 250 0331 Fax: 0114 250 0676 www.northend.co.uk

Acknowledgements:
Without generous personal and company sponsorship from a number of sources, this book could not have been produced, and the Ken Hawley Collection Trust is deeply grateful to the following individuals and companies:

Lead Sponsors:

Dormer Tools Ltd
Hugh M Facey MBE
John Jewitt
Sheffield Industrial Museums Trust

Supporting Sponsors:

William Beckett Plastics Ltd
Burgon and Ball Ltd
Peter E Curtis
John A Dormer
Noel Edwards
Field Enterprise Ltd
Thomas Flinn & Co
Christopher J Jewitt
The James Neill Trust Fund
Robert Sorby Ltd
The Hugh and Ruby Sykes Charitable Trust

Main cover image is a view of steel and file manufacturers John Bedford & Sons Ltd, c..1900 showing the large Lancashire boiler providing power for forging and grinding. In the foreground are several large wheels, probably used for file grinding.

Contents

Inside back cover 'Sheffield Year Knife'

My grateful thanks are due, primarily to Ken Hawley for his inestimable time in imparting a great deal of his boundless knowledge of tools and their use, over countless hours of talks and meetings, also to his wife Emily for her forbearance.

Similarly to the Museum Trustee, management, staff and volunteers, some for reading or providing advice and commenting on provisional drafts, giving logistical support and assisting with archival material, and for allowing access to Abbeydale Industrial Hamlet. Thanks also go to the Custodian and volunteers at Wortley Top Forge who facilitated the use of their site for certain photographs, together with Pete Goss at his forge and workshop within Kelham Island Museum.

Also, special thanks for graphic design and image manipulation by the designer and team of my friends Alan Gray in London and Tim Mackey in Sheffield.

Permission to use some archive and photographic material has been given by Keith Crawshaw, Stanley UK Holding Ltd., Bowers Metrology and Lloyds Pharmacy. Attempts have been made to trace original copyright of other images used in this publication, but changes in company ownership over the years has meant that some names may have been missed, for which I apologise.

All full-page product photography has been digitally imaged by Mark Crapper, M C Photography, 2A Waverley Works, Effingham Road, Sheffield S4 7YP Tel. 0114 272 2275.

Timber background material for photography was loaned by courtesy of Hector & Cedric Ltd., Ecclesall Wood Sawmill, Abbey Lane, Sheffield, S7 2QZ Tel. 0114 235 6436.

Smaller photographs within the text were imaged by the author, some with studio facilities provided by Allan Parker ARPS.

I am also very appreciative of the trust placed in me by Alex Pettifer, Chairman of SIMT for inviting me to undertake this project.

Finally, sincere thanks to my wife Barbara, sometimes for her typing and proofreading skills, but mostly for her continued patience and understanding during the production period.

Museums are about objects and collections and for people. Their job is to build those collections, to afford them the best possible care, and to reveal the wealth and diversity of the meanings inherent in them. In the Hawley Collection, Sheffield has not only an outstanding collection of extraordinary depth and range, and an asset of national and international significance, but an unparalleled inheritance that reflects the life's work, the inspiration and the unrivalled understanding of one man—Ken Hawley. Born and bred in Sheffield he has spent his life closely associated with the tool and cutlery trades and the collection he has amassed is the outcome of his profound knowledge of the industry.

There is no other comparable collection relating to the history, technology and evolution of tools and cutlery and their manufacture. It is important at a number of levels. It reflects the industries that have made the name of Sheffield famous throughout the world and so is a crucial element in the city's own cultural heritage. It charts the development of tool and cutlery manufacturing and as such represents an internationally important resource for historians. And, through its creator, it has benefited from someone whose knowledge and insight has resulted in a collection of immense strength and scope and who continues to apply his erudition and experience to its wellbeing.

It is a mark of the importance of the collection that ownership has been transferred to a special trust, the Ken Hawley Collection Trust. Secondly, the University of Sheffield provided storage and study space that enabled Ken to lead a major programme of cataloguing and, latterly, Sheffield Industrial Museums Trust has provided it with a permanent home. Today it is accessible to the public, through the galleries at Kelham Island and in the well-housed and impeccably ordered wealth of objects that lie behind the public displays.

I have known Ken Hawley for some forty years and in that time have come to value and respect his huge fund of knowledge and, most especially, his lively and limitless generosity in sharing it with anyone who wants to know, to look and to listen. To that might be added his ready willingness to explain by holding and handling and demonstrating, for it is in the tactile nature of much of the Hawley Collection that its secrets lie. Tools are there to be used, their qualities best appreciated by how effectively they fit the purpose for which they were designed and made. There is craftsmanship in their making and craftsmen used them and the highly personal nature of the relationship between the one and the other was part of what made Sheffield so special. Huge numbers of specialist trades and processes benefited from tools tailor-made in Sheffield for their specific requirements, be it a pair of scissors, a handsaw, plane or file. All these subtleties of manufacture and use can be found here in the Hawley Collection.

Sir Neil Cossons
Rushbury, Shropshire
March 2011

I consider it a great honour to have been asked to write this book and to be associated in a small way, both as a supplier and later as a colleague with someone like Ken Hawley, a down to earth character and a true Yorkshireman. Ken has devoted all of his life to the tool trade, and when in business was known for ensuring that his customers had the best tools and advice for their particular need at the time. He is a veritable fount of knowledge on materials, tools, their history and the way they are used and taken to market, not only English tools, but from worldwide manufacturers. His thirst for information led him to start the collection, which now numbers over 100,000 items. As an adjunct to this, there are an additional 70,000 or so catalogues, lists and manufacturers' papers, drawings, photographs and the like, and it is no wonder that for many years he has become known affectionately as the 'Collector'.

To do full justice to this immense collection in print, would need a book at least ten times this size, which is simply not a feasible proposition, so what has been aimed for in the fourteen main chapters, is to focus on 'trades', and within these, identifying perhaps the most significant and interesting items and artefacts. Some of these will be illustrated to demonstrate either generic or particular features, and be accompanied by brief text with names and descriptive details.

Tools, and particularly old craftsmen's tools, almost always evoke a feeling of nostalgia in which history plays its part, as Sheffield's traditions and excellence of its edge tools can be traced back to the period prior to the Industrial Revolution. Indeed, one John Leland, a diarist and itinerant traveller around England in the reign of Henry VIII, returned several times to Hatfield, Doncaster and Sheffield and wrote, 'Ther be many smiths and cutlers in Hallamshire', and in a further note, 'veri good smithies for all cuttinge tooles'.

Demand for higher quality steel to produce a better and lasting cutting edge meant that by the early 16th Century, Sheffield's craftsmen had started to import their raw materials from Spain, Germany and Sweden, the latter being considered to be of the finest quality. Despite the huge cost of importing steel from Europe, Sheffield's location had a number of manufacturing advantages, the first of these being unlimited water power from the several streams running down the surrounding hills, and emptying into the river Don. These streams were dammed forming mill ponds, and controlled amounts of water were diverted through sluices to drive massive overshot water wheels which in turn transmitted the energy produced, through gears, pulleys and belts to power machinery for the forging or grinding of knives, scythes and other edge tools. Around this time there were some 100 mills sited along the Don, Sheaf, Porter, Rivelin, Moss, Blackburn and other watercourses. Some, like Abbeydale Works (known colloquially as Abbeydale Hamlet), are still in intermittent use today, for educational purposes, and derelict ruins of many others can be observed along these streams. Sheffield's second advantage lay in its geological position within the Coal Measures and the associated sandstones which were used in the manufacture of grinding wheels of various types and sizes. Here again, on the moors outside the City, can be found evidence of the quarries where the gritstone was cut and hewn into the shape of wheels.

Records exist showing that knives have been made in and around Sheffield since at least 1297. Successive Lords of the Manor, the Earls of Shrewsbury, were said to have taken a great interest in the trade. Skilled craftsmen in forging, grinding, finishing, handle making and the like, were used in the production of knives, scissors, files, shears, sickles and scythes. To a large extent, these skills were contained within parish boundaries, each parish specialising in the manufacture of a particular tool or operation. This necessitated some form of hierarchical structure, and when the last Earl of Shrewsbury died in 1616, Sheffield craftsmen petitioned Parliament for an Act to enable them to have control and organise the increasing number of trades and tradesmen. Eventually, in 1624 The Company of Cutlers in Hallamshire was founded with a Master Cutler, two Wardens, six Searchers and twenty-four Assistants, with the remainder of the craftsmen being known as the Commonalty. The Company had self-governing powers over the district of Hallamshire, which encompassed an area roughly 26 miles by 22 miles. Effectively, the new organisation was a craft guild and craftsmen were bound by the rules of the company which regulated the training of apprentices, quality of goods produced, together with the registered trademarks used to identify the work of each individual craftsman.

In the early days of the Cutlers' Company, Sheffield had no mayor and the Master Cutler was the senior figure in the town representing its interests, particularly in industrial matters. The Rules of the Company were strict, and enforced by a system of fines for inferior work, or misuse of registered marks which could result in destruction of the products. Over the intervening centuries the Company has changed considerably as its powers were amended by Acts of Parliament, which latterly has allowed directors and company owners in the steel trade generally, to be admitted as Freemen.

Finally, a brief mention should perhaps be made of the system known as 'Little Mesters', which thrived in Sheffield before mechanisation came along. Enterprising self-employed men would rent space within any sort of workplace, and be contracted to make a specific product, or carry out part of the manufacturing operation which then might be passed to another craftsman. Such 'little mesters,' employed and paid their own workpeople, having provided both tools and equipment as needed for the job. Materials might be purchased from the factory proprietor or on the open market, or were sometimes provided 'free of charge'. Finished goods were usually bought back by the factory owner at a previously agreed price, but at times of low demand the 'little mester' could sell elsewhere if the proprietor could not find a buyer.

Although the author of this book, I am 'nobbut the messenger', trying to convey some of Ken's wealth of knowledge to a much wider audience both young and old, and by this means, helping to preserve the collection in perpetuity.

Derek Bateson

Wortley Top Forge and cottages as extended in 1713

In 1927, Kenneth W. Hawley was born on a housing estate to the east of Sheffield. Ken Hawley MBE, as we all know him now, was the son of Isabella and Walter Hawley, a wire-goods maker, senior partner of the family firm, Wire Products. A few years later in 1932, the family moved to Wadsley, and in 1939 to a semi-detached house in the same area. This is the house where Ken and his wife still live to this day. In 1940 Ken entered Sheffield Junior Technical School, to complete his education, but circumstances dictated that in 1941, able-bodied men were having to be called up for service in the armed forces. The resulting shortage of labour meant that Ken had to leave school at fourteen to join his father's business,

Ken with the original tool which inspired the collection

making wire guards for machinery in Sheffield's manufacturing industries. By 1945 he was eligible to join the Army, which he did, being demobilised some three years later in March 1948. Ken worked for Wilks Bros., a firm of ironmongers for a short time, then moved to Jos.Gleave, a well respected, tool merchants' business in Manchester, both then and now. Two years later, Ken returned to Sheffield and joined a firm in Rotherham, J. Rhodes and Sons. He quickly became the shop manager, and about this time met his future wife Emily, an employee at the same firm. Whilst working here in 1955, Ken visited an undertaker's workshop in Rotherham. This was to demonstrate a wood planing machine for use in coffin making and it was here that he spotted on the wall, an early iron brace, later dated to around 1880. He was fascinated by this and asked if he could have it, and the brace became his very first acquisition, inspiring Ken's enthusiasm for the beauty and craftsmanship to be found in many tools of yesteryear.

1959 was a momentous year for Ken, when he embarked on a new venture by setting up his own business as a specialist tool merchant, (not as an ironmonger). The first premises were in Button Lane, before moving two years later to a new shop in Earl Street, where the business continued to trade as K.W. Hawley (Tools) Ltd. until his 'retirement' in 1989. He soon heard, through his fathers' contacts in the

trade, that cutlers Jos. Rodgers, had some interesting tools and equipment for forging knife blades; he made a visit and was given an old forging hammer and some examples of blades, forged by one of their last skilled hand forgers. Then in 1965, the famous toolmakers Wm. Marples was about to close their plane-making department, so Ken took the opportunity to film for posterity, the manufacture of beech-wood planes. A short time later he acquired all the tools used for manufacturing these, even the plane-makers' benches. Another major manufacturer to close in Sheffield at a later date was Rabone Chesterman, manufacturers of rules and measuring equipment, located at Bow Works in Pomona Street, now a listed building. Of course Ken got there first and bought two Societé Genevoise screw dividing machines and other equipment. These SG precision machines were used for accurately producing or dividing, ranges of scales for vernier caliper gauges. No mention has yet been made of Ken's own house where the garage had been given a second storey to provide more space. This also became full to overflowing, as did two large wooden garden sheds, and the house's attic, home to thousands of old documents and irreplaceable catalogues. Indeed, the weight was so much that the bedroom ceiling developed a bow! Outside the house, even the front perimeter 'fence' is made up of worn grinding stones; an anvil features in the wrought-iron gates which also carries a sign for Wortley Top Forge, where Ken was Custodian for 40 years.

In 1991, as a visitor to the Ruskin Gallery, Ken met by chance the Curator, Janet Barnes and explained his predicament regarding space for his collection. Fired by his enthusiasm, Janet agreed that the collection deserved to be seen by a wider public, and plans were put in place, culminating in a major exhibition 'The Cutting Edge' at the Ruskin in 1992, featuring a representative selection of tools and artefacts housed in fourteen large showcases.

The exhibition attracted a record-breaking 26,000 visitors from every walk of life, many having been employed in the tool and allied trades. Soon afterwards, meetings were convened, the first at the Cutlers Hall which resulted in an Action Group, to look into ways of preserving the collection for posterity. The group, led by John Jewitt, Chairman of Footprint Tools, the last private tool manufacturing company in the City, met again at George Wostenholme's old mansion at Nether Edge, and with help and finance from Sheffield University and others, the Ken Hawley Collection Trust came into being. In 1993 at the age of 66, Ken was quoted as saying *'One day I should like to see a museum of tools and tool-making here in Sheffield. Meanwhile, I've got fifty years of knowledge in my head that needs cataloguing and I'm still learning!'*

An unused building, formerly a steel warehouse for S & C Wardlow, was purchased by the University of Sheffield, refurbished and fitted with secondhand racking, and piece by piece the collection was moved from several temporary sites around the City to what was re-named the Hawley Building in 1995. At about that time, Ken became affectionately known as 'The Collector', a fitting title some may say. Also in 1995, Ken was awarded an Honorary Fellowship by Sheffield Hallam University, to commemorate his service both to Wortley Top Forge and the tool collection. This was followed in 1998 by the award of an MBE, fittingly presented on behalf of Her Majesty the Queen, by the Earl of Scarborough.

By 2002, full registered museum status had been achieved by the collection, with cataloguing and archiving being a continual process, as well as more items being added to the collection. So much so that by 2007 the Hawley Building was bulging at the seams and urgent action needed to be taken in order to preserve this historical gem.

The following chapter aims to define the new Gallery vision and concept with its purpose-designed interpretative displays, research and storage facilities.

S & C Wardlow's poster, from the early 1900's, illustrating their two works. The left-hand view shows the Portobello site, and the extreme right-hand building is the only surviving part. Once the steel warehouse, it housed the Hawley Collection for some fifteen years up to 2010.

Derelict Russell Works building in 2008   ©Keith Crawshaw

Partial view of the new gallery from the same viewpoint

©Derek Bateson

n 2007 an idea was put forward to re-house the Hawley Collection. The Sheffield Industrial Museums Trust and the Ken Hawley Collection Trust then worked closely together, developing a vision to renovate, restore and revitalise the last derelict building on the Kelham Island Museum site to provide a new permanent home to the collection. Appropriately, the building designated was Russell Works, former premises to Sheffield saw makers, Wheatman & Smith.

An application was made for Heritage Lottery funding and in March 2008, this was confirmed as successful, allowing work to begin on creating a purpose designed gallery complete with exhibition areas, storage and research facilities. This gave a new lease of life and meant that for the first time, the collection would be on one site, allowing its full potential to be demonstrated. Building work was completed in August 2009, since when there has been a phased relocation of items from several stores around the City, with the gallery being formally opened by Sir Neil Cossons in March 2010.

The new gallery and exhibition provides an interactive visitor journey to demonstrate both the range and scope of this unique collection. It encourages active exploration of the history of Sheffield's manufacturing heritage through the considerable technological and social changes over the past 300 years. The exhibition itself consists of four discrete but interconnected areas, 'Starting the Journey', 'Investigating Design', 'Investigating Making', and 'Investigating Selling', which allows the visitor to choose their own route around the displays.

'Starting the Journey' gives a brief illustrated history of Ken Hawley, the 'Collector', early days of the collection, some of Sheffield's craftsmen, the birth of the museum, and the 2010 re-location to Kelham Island Museum. The wide diversity of tools, cutlery and artefacts is presented in an A-Z display on a wall adjacent to the area re-creating Ken's Earl Street tool merchants' shop. Here the visitor can step behind the 'counter', and learn about the 'stockroom'.

'Investigating Design' encourages visitors to think about, identify and understand how design choices may be affected through change in shape, material or the manufacturing process. On entering the gallery a large 'I see saws' wall demonstrates saw making through time and features a very wide range of designs made and developed in the City, from a delicate piercing saw to the massive circular saw blade.

'Investigating Making' looks at the often numerous stages in many manufacturing processes, at the same time celebrating the skills, craftsmanship and the hard working life endured by the Sheffield workpeople. Demonstrations on a workbench in this area will help showcase some of the skills and techniques and tools used, aided by the use of AV displays.

'Investigating Selling' examines the sources of many of the raw materials used by the various trades through the City's worldwide connections and its export markets. Advertising packaging and promotion of many famous Sheffield brands is featured here, as well as the importance of trade stands and engineering exhibitions. A small display highlights some of the ubiquitous DIY tools developed and produced in Sheffield; many visitors will have a tool or two with the famous 'Made in Sheffield' in their toolbox or garage.

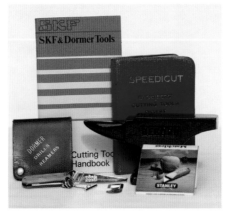

Promotional aids

Alongside the main gallery themes, visitors are encouraged to 'Investigate More', either by looking at current displays, exploring resource material, listening to and viewing AV screens, entering into family games, or just leaving a comment or enquiry note. With over 100,000 items (and still growing), the collection is unique in its diversity and scope, with only a small percentage on show at any one time. With this in mind, the gallery has been designed to allow regular changing of display units to exhibit different tool or product selections and stories. Much, but not all of this vast collection will remain in the store, on the specially strengthened mezzanine level above the display area, partly visible through windows when viewed from the gallery floor.

The Ken Hawley Collection is a rich resource and is readily available for research, loan material, temporary displays and educational purpose. Appointments may be made to view or access elements from the storage areas, and at the ground floor entrance to the gallery, a room has been set aside for facilties for interested visitors and researchers.

The next fourteen chapters provide a brief illustrated overview into Sheffield's manufacturing trades heritage, featuring some of the tools, cutlery and artefacts,contained within this incomparable collection.

This first chapter does not cover any particular trade as the subsequent sections will focus on tools and artefacts used in a multitude of trades which became established in Sheffield and the surrounding area. Instead it is felt that it would be more useful to select and briefly mention some of the many raw materials and manufacturing processes used in producing tools for these trades. As steel of one type or another was the basic raw material used in most local industries, this has been given particular attention here.

All tools used for cutting, namely chisels, knives and the like, were made of steel capable of taking and holding a keen cutting edge, in order that they would cut and work efficiently. Over the years from the 17th Century onwards, Sheffield made steel has been acknowledged as the world leader for quality and innovation. Initially this would have been shear steel, a product particularly suited for the production of butchers and table knives which became widely acclaimed worldwide. Many other types and grades of steel were invented and developed in Sheffield including blister steel, shear spring steel and chisel steel and, depending on the end use, these might be rolled into shapes or sections to reduce grinding on later manufacturing processes. Some 70 or more basic shapes were available in hundreds of sizes, also many steel qualities,

Walk & Talk:

Phrase describing the smooth opening and closing action of a spring knife.

and these like tools were catalogued in the industry's bible, The Sheffield Illustrated List, copies of which are in the Hawley collection.

Around 1740, Benjamin Huntsman, a clockmaker who had experimented in secret to produce better steel for clock springs, developed the production of crucible cast steel. This was the first commercially made steel to be melted in a clay pot at high temperature to make it homogeneous, and it was from this steel that Sheffield's

Chine:

To cut through anything.

hand forgers, grinders and cutlers produced the finest tools and cutlery which established the City's reputation for quality in these trades.

Later, in 1913, Harry Brearley, a Sheffield steelworks chemist, discovered stainless steel, a metal we are all familiar with, and without which the world could not survive today. It is extensively used worldwide in hospitals, chemical and petroleum industries, for aerospace and marine applications, as well as the more familiar cutlery we use every day in our homes.

The earliest reference to metal production in the Sheffield area dates back to the 10th Century when monks from

1.13

Blister steel bar

a

b

c

d

e

f

g

h

i

j

k

l

I.14

a) Tortoiseshell
Unpolished and polished examples

b) Mother of Pearl Shell
From Manilla or Australia

c) Giraffe Bone
From Africa

d) Grey Buffalo Horn
From South America

e) Black Buffalo Horn
From Indonesia

f) Stag Horn
Probably Chital, from India

g) Sambar Horn
(Section), from India

h) Narwhal Horn
From Arctic Ocean

i) Crucible Cast Steel
Sample box

j) Best Double Shear Steel
The inset image illustrates the mark used by the trade to define the steel quality

k) Knife Handles
Moulded and laminated patterns

l) Stainless Steel
Mirror finish

Kirkstead Abbey in Lincolnshire, built an iron works on the Blackburn Brook between Ecclesfield and Wincobank, and the first cutler was recorded about a century later.

Saw making was revolutionised around the middle of the 18th Century when crucible cast steel, together with new rolling techniques enabled the production of sheet steel of unprecedented quality. This gave Sheffield entry to worldwide markets, particularly America where its axes and saws were much in demand for cutting down the vast swathes of forest to enable their arable economy to develop.

Sheffield's edge tool trades as they became known, roughly divided into 'Light Edge Tools', including chisels, gouges, plane irons, drawing knives etc., and 'Heavy Edge Tools', comprising axes, adzes, bills, hooks, hatchets, choppers and similar implements, all of which were generally sold in dozens. Most of these tools required handles, the longer of which might be made of Ash or Hickory with those for the smaller hand tools generally of Box or Beech.

Other raw materials were used in the manufacture of handles or scales for the cutlery and knife trade and these varied from Ivory, Tortoiseshell, Stag's horn and Buffalo, through to the more modern Xylonite which was first produced in 1870. Ebony, Mahogany, Rosewood and other tropical hardwoods were also used for cutlery and some for high quality joiners' tools, including squares, bevels, gauges, spokeshaves and levels.

The Hawley Collection of tools and cutlery helps to celebrate Sheffield's achievements as a world leader in this field, and encourages modern research establishments to continue with their work of developing new materials and techniques.

Thumb mark: A patch or mark on the pile (reverse), side of a table knife blade, where the iron tang and bolster iron has been welded to the shear steel blade.

Agon: An inverted chisel, fitted cutting edge uppermost in a socket on the forger's anvil to cut off the mood.

1.15

1.16

SUPERIOR MALLEABLE STEEL BLADES & FORKS

a

b

c

d

e

f

a) Wood Chisel Blades
Three sizes as drop forgings, before other manufacturing operations are performed

b) Chisel Blades
'Goff', machine forged

c) Full Mortice Chisel
Three 'handling' stages

d) Engineers' Hammer
Finished tool, and drop forgings showing progress from bar stock

e) Knife Blade and Fork Blanks
'Malleable Steel' blanks, in Travellers' sample case. Offered to the lower end of the cutlery trade

f) Sterling Silver Spoons
Stages from bar stock, hand wrought, filed, buffed and polished. Still produced in 2011 by Fletcher Robinson in Sheffield

These old photographs show the ivory and stag's horn stores at cutlery manufacturers Joseph Rodgers, circa 1912. Ivory and stag horn was regularly used for handle manufacture of many quality cutlery items and the stag store illustrates both the variety and quantity used by a single cutlery company. Their products might range from table and carving knives, steels, open razors, also pen and pocket knives'.

This is one of the largest sections, with a tremendous range of tools for working wood. Indeed woodworking goes back a very long way, even to the stone axes used in the Neolithic period around 3000 BC, although there are no tools of this type in the collection.

All woodworking and its associated range of tools, stem from the basic raw material the tree, which first has to be cut down, then follows the shaping and marking of all the wooden components for buildings and their associated furniture. Depending on size, trees were felled with an axe and the two-man cross cut saw. The resulting logs were then sawn into boards with pit saws up to 8ft in length, a

Bellus or belluses:

A forger's bellows. Often used in the double plural form.

Hafting: Attaching the handle to a knife or tool.

very tiring job. From the early 19th Century, power driven circular saws took over most of this manual work. These timber boards were used in many areas to make floorboards, windows and doors by joiners. Their first job was to mark out the timber for subsequent shaping or finishing after cutting to lengths with hand saws.

Sheffield, from the mid 18th century, dominated the world in saw production for about 150 years. Planing wood to size was next, initially by hand, then after c.1850 planing machines were introduced, and their steel cutting blades were all made in Sheffield. Hundreds of patterns of moulding planes to produce different wood profiles were made country wide but these too, all had their cutting blades made in Sheffield.

Setting out tools for making joints included gauges, squares and levels, each made in many patterns and sizes in Beech-wood, Boxwood,

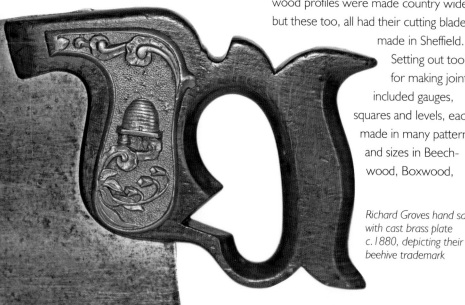

Richard Groves hand saw with cast brass plate c.1880, depicting their beehive trademark

a) Joiners' Hammer, Exeter Pattern
Steel faced, wrought iron head. 18th Century

b) Hammer
*Specific use unknown, but possibly for shoe, saddlers' or upholstery trades.
Early 19th Century*

c) Chamfer Shave
Made in bronze material, with patented adjustment feature, by E Preston, Birmingham, late 19th Century

d) Cutting Gauge
Ebony and nickel silver, made for the 1851 Great Exhibition

e) Panel Saw
(Approx 21" long, but thought to be cut down) London pattern handle with three brass washers, and pinned with iron rivets. Made by Richard Groves, 18th Century

f) Hand Saw, 28"
Cast brass plate featuring 'Beehive' device, trademark of Richard Groves and Sons, c.1880

g) Back Saw, 20"
Brass back and London pattern handle with three screws. Made by Brightmore, late 18th Century

h) Back Saw, 16"
*Wrought iron back, London pattern handle attached with two brass screws.
Mid 18th Century*

i) Coachmakers' Brass 'Spider' Bevel
Fully adjustable, and made by E Preston, Birmingham. Late 19th Century

2.18

a

b

c

d

e

f

2.19

g

h

i

a

b

c

d

e

f

g

h

i

a) Planemakers' Wedge Plane
Beechwood, designed to cut the wedge as shown below plane in image. William Marples, 19th Century

b) Cabinetmakers' Shoulder Plane
Made in bronze and Rosewood by Charles Bayfield

c) Cabinetmakers' Rebate Plane
With variable pitch adjustment. Made in France c.1845

d) Joiners' Boxwood fourfold Rule
Graduated in Russian Verschoks (1 Verschok = 1¾" approx)

e) Rulemakers' Boxwood 'Apprentice Piece'
Markings are of numerous foreign measures and figure sizes. Made at Cox of Birmingham 1862

f) Shipwrights' Adze
Of exhibition quality construction, with round eye hole and polished handle. Adze blade carries engraved bulls' head, the trademark of Marsh Brothers, Sheffield. Mid 19th Century

g) Instrument Makers Iron Plane
Used for producing straight edges on metal rules. Early 19th Century

h) Planemakers' Top Float
Used in the making of Moulding Planes. Wm Marples, 19th Century

i) Planemakers' Side Float
Use in the making of Bench Planes. This tool is shown in its sharpening block. Wm Marples, 19th Century

Rosewood and Ebony. The marked out joints were cut with steel chisels, available in sizes from ⅛in (3mm) to 2in (50mm) or more. There were many blade strengths and lengths, usually with parallel blades, except for the Chinese chisel which had a blade which splayed out towards the cutting edge. Chisels, and similar tools like gouges for shaping concave profiles, were made with a wide variety of differing handles. These many differences came about because millwrights, joiners, wheelwrights, cabinet makers and other trades, required their own specialist tools.

One very interesting and versatile tool was the drawing knife. Basically this had a strong steel blade, sharpened on one edge, with handles set on right angled tangs at either end. These were used by pulling towards the user with rapid stock removal and good finishes being achieved.

Other tools for woodworking included hammers, braces, bits, augers and screwdrivers (always called 'turnscrews' in Sheffield until about 1960). These too were made in a wide variety of patterns, sizes and qualities for the home trade and export to all over the world.

Last and certainly not least, the collection includes literally thousands of wood and/or metal, woodworking planes of many types, only a few of which can be illustrated here.

Broddle: To enlarge, or ream out a hole, e.g., in a haft or handle, to fit the blade tang.

Ass hoil, ass nook: The place under a grate where ashes drop.

Robert Marples Boxwood and plated joiners' brace with pearl inlaid ebony head. Made for mid 19th Century exhibition

2.22

Set of 29 stairmakers' planes, made and used by John S Waddington in New York. One of the smallest is shown with a 50p coin for comparison

Like woodworking, builders' and plumbers' trades cover a number of sub-trades, each dependent upon and interacting with each other. Perhaps the best example of this might be likened to the building of a new property when various trades work together or follow a set pattern in the construction process.

In Sheffield and the surrounding areas one could consider some of the quarrying tools, hammers, mallets, chisels, scutches, bolsters for stone dressing, crowbars and Lewises (a simple lifting device for heavy stones) etc., used to produce and move blocks of sandstone. Or, using another building method, brickmaking tools would be used, together with clay spades and brick moulds, originally made from wood and producing single bricks, but today mass-produced on a production line. As construction progresses, scaffolders, masons and bricklayers have their own tools including hammers, trowels for bricklaying, pointing and gauging, plus plumb-lines, line pins and a range of tape measures, rules, levels and the like.

Similarly painters and decorators have a specific range of 'cutlery', including paint scrapers, scissors, putty and palette knives. Paviors and roofers each have specialist trade tools encompassing slate rules, slaters' saxes for trimming slates, with a sharpened 'pick' at one end to produce the nail hole by which the slate was secured to the roof timbers, also rippers for removing damaged slates, to name but a few.

In the world of building there is an overlap with roofers and plumbers who traditionally carry out the installation of leadwork and flashing on roofs and around chimneys, which also necessitates the use of specific tools and equipment. A good example is that of a plumber's hammer which has a wedge-shaped pein, at the opposite end to the actual hammer head, and set in line with the handle. This enabled it to be used for dressing lead into seams and corners. Soldering was a means of joining lead sheet and pipework and the earliest example of a petrol blowlamp, used for lead and other work, was one invented in 1882 by C R Nyberg in Sweden.

Shell: Decorative detail on the head of the screw in scissors. Produced by filing a series of lines.

Arseboard: A board slung from behind the grinder to serve as a seat. It extends forwards between his legs to the wheel. His weight, when sitting on it, converts it into a powerful lever for pressing any objects to be ground, onto the stone.

3.23

Original pattern Nyberg blowlamp

3.24

a) Brick Mould
Wooden frame with metal facings

b) Scaffolders' Hammer
Multipurpose tool, for wooden pole and rope scaffold construction. Mid 1930's

c) Plasterers' Lath Axe
With strapped handle for added strength

d) Brick Hammer
Devon pattern, with square head

e) Slaters' Hammer
Scotch pattern, strapped, and with side claw

f) Paviors' Hammer
Used for laying paving stones and sets

g) Millwrights' Socket Mortice Chisel
3¼" wide, used on heavy timber structures, lock gates and barn doors

h) Masons' Drag
Used for shaping and dressing Bath stone on construction and repair work

i) Slate Splitting Chisel
With mallet head and used for Welsh blue slate

j) Slaters' Saxe
For roofing repairs, cutting slates to size and making nail holes

k) Brick Trowels
These demonstrate wear and tear through continuous use. Most probably 19th Century

l) Plasterers' Joint Rule
Used for making mitres on ceiling plaster mouldings

m) Plasterers' Margin Trowel
For recessing work in difficult to reach areas when plastering. 19th Century

n) Plasterers' Trowel and Square
For producing fine detail plaster work. 20th Century

Later production models were made and sold by Max Sievert who ultimately took over the company. Some ten years later, another Swedish engineer F W Lindquist adapted Nyberg's design, setting it in a brass frame on which a small cooking utensil could stand, and re-directing the burner to face upwards. He patented this device and the Primus stove was born. Plumbers used lead ladles, melting pots and soldering irons of many designs, alongside a wide variety of lead dressing tools and bossing mallets, all of which were made in Boxwood as were turn-pins for opening out lead piping. Various solders, also resins and tallow as fluxes were used in the processes of sealing lead joints.

An associated trade of builders and plumbers is that of glaziers as almost all buildings have windows, necessitating the use of glaziers' diamonds for cutting glass panels. Glaziers use special rules and T-squares, and these are specially notched to allow the glass cutting diamond to reach to the edge of the glass sheet.

Burnt blades: Blades overheated at the wheel which spoils the temper of the steel.

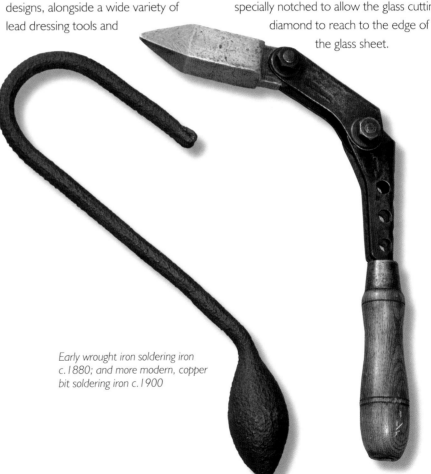

Early wrought iron soldering iron c.1880; and more modern, copper bit soldering iron c.1900

3.25

Drop stamp at Wortley Top Forge. Originally from Silversmiths C W Fletcher in Sheffield, and used for 'bowling' solid silver table spoons

a) Bobbin
Made of Lignum vitae and used for pulling through, and opening out, deformed lead pipe

b) Petrol Blowlamp
Original design by C R Nyberg, and made by Max Sievert 1882

c) Pliers
Used on old-style gas burners

d) Tallow Candles and Case
In original tin case, and used for lead pipe jointing

e) 'Patent' Jointing Tool
Used for forming ends of lead pipe joints before soldering

f) 'Patent' Lead Pipe Cutters
Used for cutting pipe ends square

g) Soldering Iron
With copper bit and adjustable shank for soldering copper c.1900

h) Soldering Iron
Early wrought iron example, used on lead roof works c.1880

i) 'Moleskin' Wiping Cloth
Used for 'wiping' and smoothing lead soldered joints

j) 'U' Tube Manometer
For testing and measuring gas pressure in pipes

k) Lead Cutting Knife
For sheet lead, with riveted leather handle scales

l) Washer Cutter
Adjustable, for producing leather washers

m) Plumbers' Straight Pein Hammer
Possibly used for seating lead sheet into tight corners

n) Lead 'Dummy'
With cane handle and 'wiped' lead head, for straightening damaged pipework

o) Gas Burner Combination Tool
This tool consists of a turnscrew, taper reamer, taper and parallel taps, and a die

p) Glaziers' Nailing Hammer
Flat-faced and square ended for accurate striking

q) Glass Cutter
Adjustable radius, for cutting circles out of glass sheet

r) Glaziers' Pliers
Designed to grip and break off glass edges to size

s) Wheel Glass Cutter
Made of brass, with three handle notches for breaking glass of different thicknesses

a

b

c

f

e

d

k

3.27

g

i

j

h

m

n

l

q

r

s

o

p

3.28

ODE TO A SQUARE

Oh, lovely Square, in thy straight lines
Is proof of mankind's skill
To seize and rend the naked Steel
And make it do his will.

For after all, tho' curves and bends
Are well within our plan,
The secret of thy dead straight lines
Is scarcely known to man.

Thy simple shape, oh siren bright,
Thou layest like a snare,
To steal away the brains of men,
And make them tear their hair.

But now, at last, we know thy wiles,
Thou'rt vanquished evermore,
Thou'rt made in several sizes now,
From two to twenty-four.

In paper soft thou'rt wrapped and placed,
Well greased, in wooden box,
And sent to where that prudent chap,
The dealer, keeps good stocks.

And when at last thou'rt lifted from
Thy prison walls so wooden,
Whoever sees thee will exclaim
"By Jove! this is a Good'un"

Extracted from Moore & Wright (Sheffield) Ltd,
Catalogue No 31 dated 1932
Reproduced by kind permission of Bowers Metrology

The Ken Hawley Collection is probably unique in the number of tools and artefacts it contains, across a wide spectrum of specialist trades, ranging from basketmakers, bellhangers and boilermakers, through to upholsterers and sailmakers, to name only a few. Some of the other trades might have included brushmakers, thatchers, bookbinders, gunsmiths and these and many others are all represented with their specialised tools and equipment.

Farriers and blacksmiths, notably in country areas, apart from their large heavy anvils, used a wide range of paring knives, pincers, tongs and other tools. The associated trade of saddlery, used round-bladed head and collarmakers' knives, seam turners, edge irons and cutters, hand palms, stuffing rods, and of course special 'pricking' and other punches and a wide variety of straight and curved needles for sewing leather.

Cannelled edge:
The chamfered edge of a tool, knife or razor when the fetheredge has been removed.

Somewhat similar tools might be used for shoemaking and sailmaking, with coachmakers having specially made wooden compass planes, which were designed for smoothing concave or convex surfaces such as coach doors and their frames. Later, metal planes could be adjusted for either application as they had a flexible metal sole plate. Shipwrights also used many different caulking irons or chisels together with mallets for sealing joints in ships' timbers.

Almost everything that we make and use has to be measured in some shape or form in order to achieve consistency and fit. Rules are a good example, and the earliest dated rule in the collection carries the date 1768 and is made of Boxwood. There are in excess of one thousand Boxwood rules and gauges here at the Hawley Collection, and all these were made for use by joiners, millwrights,

Chesterman Cattle Gauge

Stiddy: Local name for anvils of which there were many patterns made in and used for the Sheffield tool and cutlery trades.

Bull week: The week before Christmas, when the cutlers 'bulled at work', or made an extra effort.

bricklayers, stonemasons and other similar trades, generally up to four feet in length. There are examples of wooden slide rules, used for complex calculations well before computers were invented. They were used by draughtsmen and architects together with textile and mechanical engineers for calculating dimensions, volumes and weights of steel and iron bars, as well as many other materials.

The first steel measuring tape in the world was invented and made in Sheffield by James Chesterman in 1842. Among other similar products he produced a 'cattle gauge', which was a tape for farmers to measure and value cattle before purchase, using a series of complicated calculations to roughly assess the weight of the animal. Many patterns of steel, also linen tape measures were produced for measuring applications worldwide. Steel rules, some straight, others folding, were also made and after 1870 it was possible to divide an inch into 100 equal divisions, so fine that they needed to be viewed through a magnifying eyeglass. The Hawley Collection contains hundreds of patterns, designed for many specific purposes.

Towards the end of the 19th Century, machinery and metal machining was starting to become more and more accurate, necessitating sophisticated measuring equipment. The micrometer, a

4.29

Ciceri Smith's Micrometer

a) **Upholsterers' Cabriolet Hammer**
London pattern

b) **Coach Trimmers' Hammer**

c) **Upholsterers' Hammer**
London pattern

d) **Upholsterers' Pincers**

e) **Saddlers' Half Moon Knife**

f) **Upholsterers' Web Stretcher**

g) **Carpet Stretcher**
With mushroom head

h) **Tanners' Fleshing Knife**

i) **Saddlers' Screw Shoulder Veiner**

j) **Saddlers' Stuffing Iron**

k) **Saddlers' Plough/Cutting Gauge**

l) **Curriers' Counter Knife**

m) **Shoemakers' 'Clicker'**
Sometimes termed a Stafford Knife

n) **Shoemakers' Breasting Knife**

o) **Shoemakers' Awl Blades**
*One gross (144) box,
George Barnsley, Sheffield*

p) **Shoemakers' Awl**
Patent pattern

q) **Dressmakers' Piercing Awl**

r) **Shoemakers' Peg Rasp and Knife**

s) **Shoemakers' Pincers**
Bulldog pattern

t) **Shoemakers' Cramping Hammer**

u) **Wad Punch**
For cutting out leather discs

v) **Saddlers' Crewe Punch**

w) **Shoemakers' Closing Hammer**

x) **Upholsterers' Straight Pinking Iron**

y) **Saddlers' Maul**
*With Lignum Vitae (sometimes known as
Ironwood), head*

hand held precision measuring tool was introduced, which could measure to one thousandth part of an inch, and shortly afterwards to one ten thousandth of an inch. Sheffield by this time was achieving a reputation for measuring equipment and was considered to be a centre of excellence, due to the craftsmanship developed at Chesterman's, Shardlow's, and later Moore and Wright. It is interesting to see examples of the earliest 'digital' micrometers, patented in 1893, and not really an accurate description, because they were mechanical in construction and operated through a system based on the screw thread, with only the readout in digital form. Today of course, digital micrometers are completely electronic. There are now more than 300 micrometers in the collection from all over the world, but many of them were made in Sheffield. Measuring gauges for all applications include Vernier calliper gauges, wire gauges and gun bore gauges, also measuring machines, to name but a few. All are represented here and it will be seen that the importance of measuring tools cannot be overestimated, even today.

Devil: A piece of flat steel bar, with a slit, cut part way down. This is wedged in a hole in the stiddy, and is used to straighten twisted blades.

a

b

c

d

e

f

g

h

i

j

k

l

m

n

o

p

q

r

s

t

u

v

w

x

y

4.31

Xylonite: An early form of plastic, used for knife handles.

Travellers' sample case of sail, saddlers' and shoemakers' needles and assorted awls. These were all of Sheffield manufacture

Hack hammer:

Chisel-faced, adze-shaped hammer used to correct defects in the surface of a grindstone.

a) Glove Stick Boxwood, with square taper, graduated in French and London inches. Rabone, 20th Century

b) Bushel Measure Boxwood, for testing accuracy of Bushel measures

c) Steel Standard For checking Bushel measures, Rabone 1892

d) Glaziers' 'T' Square With notched stock for cutter access

e) Tailors' Leg Stick Used in the cutting out of trouser patterns

f) Engineers' Slide Rule Boxwood, Routledge pattern with protractor and logarithmic scales on brass slide. Used as a sample pattern at John Rabone, mid 19th Century

g) Engineers' Slide Rule Boxwood, two foot, two fold. Logarithmic scales on wood slide, and tables for calculating area, volume and weight of materials. Early 19th Century

h) Ropemakers' Gauge Boxwood and brass. For calculating circumference, size and strength of Manilla cordage, and steel wire rope

i) Stonemasons' Level Boxwood Spirit Level, rule marked and with plumb. Rabone, early 20th Century

j) Calculator and Measure Boxwood, used for sizes of named paper sheet measures. Made for the Morning Post, London by John Rabone and Sons c.1900

k) Shoe Measuring Stick Graduated in inches, metric and shoe sizes

l) Cargo Calipers Used to calculate box and carton volume. Graduated in inches and $1/8$". Maker unknown, late 19th Century

m) Tailors' Square Tapered legs and graduated in inches

n) 24" Tailors' Square Boxwood and brass with tables and measures, mid 20th Century

o) Portable Metronome For 'keeping time'. Brass case and retractable linen tape, marked in beats per minute plus musical notation. James Chesterman, mid 19th Century

p) Steel Tape Concave, retractable tape measure for Surveyors. Graduated ten inches to one London foot (25.4cm). Each inch divided into tenths to measure 1/100's of a foot. James Chesterman 1930's

q) Rigid Steel Tape Measure Early pattern, with retractable concave blade and unbreakable 'Bakelite' case, c. mid 1920's. James Chesterman

r) Linen Tape 'Improved' metallic wired retractable tape measure. In leather case, marked as registered December 16th 1845 by James Chesterman. A world first.

4.33

5.34

The Sheffield Cutlery Trades, making tools or knives that cut, as opposed to flatware, spoons, forks etc., were split into six main sections—table knives for eating, pen and pocket knives with folding blades, razors for shaving, scissors, from tiny eye surgeon's scissors to large tailors' shears, trade knives and finally, surgical instruments. The latter were made of the highest quality steel and included scalpels, amputation saws, trephines for brain surgery, bullet extractors and many others. Trade knives were then classified and sub-divided into butchers' knives, leather trade knives, furriers' and pruning knives, to name just two or three examples. Also included here might be the Bowie knife for which Sheffield became famous, sheath knives, daggers and canoe knives for making birch bark canoes in Canada. Such knives were supplied through the Hudson's Bay Company for trading with the indigenous Indians. Another specialist utilitarian knife was one used by sailors, which carried a folded-down, round marlinspike, used for splicing and joining ropes.

Dolly: A log of wood placed in the wet grinder's trough to adjust the level of water to meet the face of the grindstone. Always removed after the day's work, so that the stone is not left in water.

Setting: Slightly bending and twisting scissor blades so that the edges come together and cut effectively. Bending the teeth of saws so they face alternately to each side. Both jobs carried out by hammering.

Kitt: A tub of water, used for washing and cleaning blades, to allow inspection during grinding.

Butchers' knives are particularly interesting, and Ken Hawley has personally counted some 10,401 variations, produced over a span of many years. This type of knife was generally very substantionally made, being long and broad, but varying in length and shape, some with half tangs, others full tangs, with differing riveting patterns to secure the scales on the handles. Such handles were more usually made of Beech-wood, Boxwood, Rosewood or Ebony, depending on the quality required. All blades for these knives were made from shear, or double shear steel to ensure that they retained a better cutting edge after sharpening. Following WW2, manufacture of shear steel ceased, and today almost all knives are made from stainless steel, which, as previously mentioned was first made in Sheffield. A knife with a curved blade was used by skinners or tanners for skinning animal carcasses after slaughter.

The range and application of trade knives was, and is extensive, ranging from bacon and boning knives, through counter

a) Ham Slicer Square point

b) Beef Slicer Round point

c) Steak Knife For butchers' shops and cutting meat into steaks

d) Cheese Knife

e) Ham Bone Gouge

f) Camp Knife Stamped blade

g) Cooks' Knife Solid bolster and scale tang

h) Cooks' Knife Stamped blade and scale tang

i) Camp Knife Stamped blade and scale tang

j) Bacon Rib Extractor

k) Butchers' Steel For sharpening knives. Nickel silver guard and 'fancy' handle

l) Butchers' Steel Stag handle with brass bolster and iron swivel

m) Cattle Pither Used for extracting marrow from large bones

n) Fish Knife Hand forged blade by Harry Drabble. Late 20th Century

o) Kitchen Knife Rosewood handle, 20th Century

p) Butchers' Knife Carbon steel, Beechwood handle secured by four iron pins and a brass screw

q) Skinning Knife Handle is provided with finger grips

r) Sailors' Knife Green River pattern

s) Fish Filleting Knife Rosewood handle and flexible blade

t) Boning Knife Ebony handle with scale tang

u) Butchers' Spear Point Knife

v) Pig Sticking Knife For use in abattoirs

w) Sheath Knife Ebony handle, pinned with three brass pins

x) Ham Slicer Scimitar pattern

y) 'Bushman's Friend' Knife A pattern of general purpose knife, usually carried in a sheath

z) Sailors' Knife Spear point, with Beechwood handle secured by four iron pins

a *b* *c* *d* *e* *f* *g* *h* *i* *j* *k* *l* *m* *n* *o* *p* *q* *r* *s* *t* *u* *v* *w* *x* *y* *z*

5.35

John Petty show board featuring samples from their range

John Petty Product Display

This interesting show board of 'trade knives' made up by John Petty, Garden Street, Sheffield, dates from c.1930/40. It featured in a display at a Birmingham Abattoir, when visiting butchers' could purchase knives from a trade wholesaler or merchant of butchers' equipment and supplies at the premises.

Without going into fine detail on patterns of trade knives, as well as butchers' knives, the board shows other knives for fish, ham, bread, provisions, sailors', oysters, shoemakers', painters' glaziers, line fitters and basket-makers'. Sharpening steels for keeping a keen edge on knife blades, also feature on the display. It would be very interesting to know how many orders were taken for such as sailors', shoemakers' and basket-makers' knives at this location.

The display is a visual reminder of some of the high quality tools available to tradesmen as well as casual passers-by, who could see the quality and range on offer.

The gold on black device, top centre, is a reproduction of the barrel which formed John Petty's well-known trademark.

NB. Many Sheffield cutlery and tool making companies regularly made similar show-boards or displays for use in shops and on trade counters, to promote their production range.

Hunting knife and leather sheath, made in Sheffield by George Butler

knives for grocery shop use before pre-packaging came into being, to dough knives, fish scaling knives with a saw edge, fish splitting and gutting knives, even a specific halibut knife. There were knives to chop cod into steaks, smoked salmon slicers and short oyster knives. Other knives for domestic use, included bread, butter and lard knives, also half-moon cheese knives. These and mincing knives, with rounded or square blades were made from sheet steel supplied by saw plate makers. Cooks' knives had sharp points and were often through tanged; ham knives might be longer and have rounded blade ends. Many of these knives were exported worldwide to the main meat producing areas of South America, Australia and New Zealand etc.

Other specialist knives might include

Elsin: A shoemaker's awl.

designs for cutting sheet rubber, linoleum and leather, also furriers' and farriers' knives, the latter for paring the hooves of horses before shoeing, also shoe or cobblers' knives for cutting leather of which there were many styles. Many small firms specialised in the manufacture of certain knives, farriers being a good example; others made pruning knives with hooked ends. These were made in millions for tea and coffee plantations in the Far East and South America. Here, and in North America, also the West Indies, a machete for cutting sugar cane was the tool of choice.

Finally, another tool associated with butchers, fishmongers and similar trades. This is the butchers' steel, similar in some respects to a round, tapered file. In manufacture, these might be 'file-cut' or 'knurled' completely round the tool to produce minute, file-like teeth for re-sharpening blunt knives.

Plating hammer in Tilt Shop at Abbeydale Works

Since the Middle Ages when peasants subsisted by eking out a living from the land, there was a gradual move towards the sort of agrarian capitalism present in the early 19th Century. Two significant influences were the Enclosure Acts and later the four-course rotation of crops—wheat, then a root crop, then barley or oats, followed by clover or rye grass.

It is no surprise then that a considerable number of tools were developed for better cultivation and harvesting, many made in Sheffield and the surrounding areas. Turnips, as a root crop were widely grown and many patterns of turnip hoe were provided. This is a simple bladed tool set at 90° on a long handle, pulled through the rows to remove weeds or as a singling tool to thin out the crop. A Dutch hoe with a generally smaller, narrower blade set across the line of the handle was considered more accurate and was pushed through the soil. After Enclosures, hedges needed to be maintained by the use of bill hooks and slashers, many of these being made to local patterns which evolved or were developed in many areas. Similarly, for field edges, a wide range of bagging hooks and scythes for brambles, and haymaking were used. A Crown scythe would be forged from two different steels, but cheaper Patent versions

were available. Blade lengths varied and the tang was cranked, to fit into a ring set on a curved wooden handle or snathe, and was sometimes braced to the handle with a steel rod or 'grass nail', to prevent clogging from damp grass. Sickles, similar in shape to hooks, differed in that they were generally thinner and had a saw edge for wheat and cereal crops.

Sheep shears have long been made around Sheffield, again in many designs, although they are basically a simple one-handed tool. Some are made from a single piece of steel with a single bow as a spring, others made from two steel pieces were often double-bowed or had a 'W' spring. Hay forks with long handles would have had two or three straight or more often curved tines for better grip of the dried hay. Other agricultural tools included long-bladed, wedge-shaped steel drainage spades, but in East Anglia in the fen area with light loamy soils, a wooden shovel called a Ferry tool was used. There was also a

Facing: Protecting soft iron hammer heads with a hard steel face.

Engraving: Incised decoration, using small chisel-like tools, which are sometimes pushed with a wiggling action by the engraver.

Natty money: The contribution paid to a Trades' Union or Friendly Society.

rabbit trappers' spade and sugar-beet forks with ball ends to the tines to avoid impaling the root crop, thus making handling difficult. Grain was usually stored in barns and large flat barn shovels were used to collect the swept up spilt corn.

Horticulture or garden cultivation generated another very wide range of implements ranging from simple pruning or budding knives with a curved blade, through hand trowels and forks to the larger spades, shovels and forks used on bigger garden areas up to c.1930. Any hammers in the garden were usually of the strapped type for added strength and the hammer face would be chequered to

6.39

Miniature pair of garden shears, five inches overall, with 10p (24.5mm) coin for scale

6.40

a) Coachmakers' Side Axe
For woodworking (see Chapter 2), 7" blade, ground flat on one face to achieve fine finishes on wood

b) Potato Grate, or Shovel
Used when bagging potatoes by hand

c) Dutch Hoe
With wide 12" blade, used for weeding crops in the market gardening sector

d) Brushing Hook
Socketed blade, used for trimming hedgerows

e) Hoe
Two-prong frame, and separate blade. Socketed handle

f) Ferry Tool
Made of wood, and metal shod, for use in digging fenland dykes

g) Hay Fork
Strapped pattern, head only

h) Turnip Knife with hook

i) Scythe Blade
Crown pattern, solid forged

j) Scythe Blade
Patent pattern, with riveted back

k) Bagging Hook
Cranked pattern, for close cutting, sometimes used on railway embankments

l) Sickle
With 'tedded' or serrated blade

m) Hay Knife
Patent pattern, with riveted back, and 'T' handle

n) Bill Hook
Yorkshire pattern with socketed head. Used as a chopper for hedge laying when fencing

o) Bill Hook
Thought to be a pattern originating in SW England

p) Pig Scraper with hook
Used for scraping bristles from pig carcasses after dipping carcasses in scalding water

q) Shepherd's Leg Crook
Used for catching sheep, head only

prevent slipping. Pruning shears or secateurs might have been parrot-nosed or straight bladed with Aubert's pattern having a built in spring. The 'Multicultivah' was similar to today's lopper. Grass shears were similar in design to sheep shears; these were used with garden and border shears and the patterns differ very little from those of the present day.

Yarmouth beef:
Or two-eyed beef steak (red herrings); the only beef a poor cutler could afford.

Leg vice and bench in backing shop for 'Patent' scythes at Abbeydale

Swage: Decorative ground bevel, along the back of a knife blade.

Five pruning and budding knives

Yaller belly: A grinder's nickname, owing to the yellow swarf he was covered with from his wheel.

a) Lopping Shears
'Myticuttah' patent

b) Branch Lopping Shears

c) Garden Shears
Hand forged, in iron and steel, early 19th Century

d) Garden Shears
Twin cutting blades. Late 20th Century

e) Ladies Garden Shears
20th Century

f) Hedge Clippers
Ridgeway pattern

g) Secateurs or Pruning Shears
Burman pattern

h) Secateurs
Parrot blade with wooden handles, of German origin

i) Flower Gathering Secateurs

j) Pruning Shears
Auberts pattern with integral spring

k) Pruning Shears
Sliding knife pattern, early 19th Century

l) Grass Clippers
Made of cast iron and steel. German, early 20th Century

m) Grass Hook
Solid forged blade and shank

n) Asparagus Knife
Long reach blade, serrated at end, set in wooden handle

o) Gooseberry Pruner
For pruning branches/twigs on thorny bushes. Used with a pulling action

p) Raspberry Pruner
Similar to o) but with a longer reach

a

b

c

d

f

g

e

j

h

i

k

n

m

l

o

p

6.43

Mid 19th Century 'take-out' Exhibition Knife with Ivory handle, gold inlay and bolster. The horticultural blades include a saw, raspberry hook, flower gatherer's scissors and four pruning blades, all with 'worked' backs. No makers mark

Exports, both in the past and to the present day, were and are vital to Britain's economy, and as early as the mid 17th Century, emigrants to America were given a basic list of tools which were considered necessary for survival in a foreign land. Later, from the 19th Century as can be seen from contemporary documentation, Emigrant's Tool Chests were available for purchase in many sizes. The largest of these contained some 116 items and included gimlets, chisels, axes, planes, vices and other tools. The cost in 1910 was 307 shillings and 6d (approximately £15), which at today's prices equated to some £1040. The tools would have been oiled or greased to prevent rusting on the sea voyage to the destination country, and were carefully packed in a sturdy wooden box for safe transportation, and later storage.

At this time Britain had established many colonies around the world, and a major export were products grouped under the generic title of 'plantation tools', which were made in Sheffield, and around Birmingham and the Black Country where metal goods were also produced. The term included tools such as tea and coffee pruners, rubber tappers knives and

Upglazing: Buffing a blade on a wooden wheel, dressed with glue and emery, to remove scratches and give a fine black finish.

Greasy cutler: A hafter; the man who makes, files and fits, bone and horn handles to table cutlery.

machetes, the latter having a dual purpose, not only for clearing the ground of small trees and bushes prior to planting, but later for harvesting certain crops.

Hoes were extremely important and formed a large part of Britain's exports to the colonies for a very simple reason. The local populations had bare feet and couldn't use spades as we did. Also hoes made it easier to pull through as well as break up sun-baked earth, and there were hundreds of basic patterns for this tool. Whilst referring to hoes, forks too were made to be used for tilling the soil in preparation for crops. Some had simple flat-bladed tines, others with sharp diamond shaped points which were necessary for digging into hard or heavy soils. Both hoes and forks had circular 'eye's' through which the handle was attached.

Other exports included sugar cane knives and bills, the latter being a double-edged tool complete with both a straight and a curved and sometimes hooked edge. They were much shorter and sturdier than the more traditional sugar knife or machete (referred to as a matchet) which were

Outworker: A small independent cutler, performing one or two operations in his own home, then returning the article for finishing by others.

made up to 24" in length. They were available unhandled and thus cheaper, but more usually with wooden handles, although some expensive horn handled versions were produced.

Mention has been made elsewhere of canoe knives, trade knives, sheep shears, plus castrating knives for meat producing countries like Australia, New Zealand and South America. Whaling was a large industry in certain parts of the world and flensing knives from Sheffield were supplied for this trade.

For a city famous for steel it is not surprising therefore that many types of steel were exported and one of the largest exports was of saw plate, used for the production of wood saws in particular. Grindstones were another major export, and at one time during the 19th Century many stones used for saw making by the Disston Saw Company in Philadelphia, together with other manufacturers in the USA, came from quarries around Wickersley near Rotherham. Disston at that time was probably the world's largest saw manufacturer. Also, what is not generally known is that during lean times for workers in Britain, some of our skilled craftsmen, particularly from the saw trade, were 'exported' to the USA, usually on a temporary basis, until trade here improved again.

7.45

a

b

c

f

g

d

7.46

h

i

e

j

k

l

m

n

a) Plantation Hoe
With eye for fixing handle, and diamond point blade. Used in South American markets

b) Plantation Hoe
Eyed, Caroline pattern

c) Wheat or Weed Hoe
Eyed, with short neck and riveted blade

d) Potato Fork
With flat prongs, and socketed 'T' handle. Modern 21st Century, from Bulldog Tools

e) Coffee Plantation Fork
Note much larger size than d), Long, strapped handle. Used in Ceylon (Sri Lanka) in mid 20th Century, made by Bulldog Tools

f) Sugar Cane Knife
Wooden handle

g) Machete
Of unknown origin or pattern

h) Machete
Boxwood handle, and original sheath. Used by troops engaged in jungle warfare. Early 20th Century

i) Machete
Riveted handle with leather scales

j) Machete
Riveted handle made with pressed Buffalo horn scales

k) Sugar Cane Knife
Beechwood and shaped handle

l) 'Kalaboza' Machete
This machete has a squared end, or point, and handle has horn scales

m) 'Pickaroon'
Useful hand tool for moving small logs or planks of timber in the logging industry of North America

n) Tomahawk
One of several similar patterns of light axe exported to Canada and North America in the 19th Century and used by the native American tribes

Buffing: Highly polishing a blade on a leather covered wooden wheel. The leather is dressed with emery or other fine abrasive. Leather originally used was buffalo hide, leading to 'buffing'.

Ceiling mounted line shafting and belting for driving machinery at Wortley Top Forge Joiners' Shop

Dead horse: Doing work for which the cutler has already subbed, or drawn money in advance.

Whittle: An early knife, carried in a sheath on the person and used as a general purpose knife.

London pattern Blacksmiths' anvil with a pointed 'pike' or 'beak'

Smithing: Striking a blade with a chisel-faced hammer to correct any flatness errors caused by the hardening process; hand hammering a machine made spring knife blade.

a, b, c, d, and e) Pruning Knives
These hand forged, wooden handled pruning knives have minor pattern variations to suit local needs. They are used in tea, coffee, sisal or other plantations in many different parts of the world

f, g, h, i, and j) Rubber Tappers Tools
The five items are a selection of wooden handled knives/gouges used for incising the bark, or 'tapping', rubber trees, Ficus elastica, for their sap (latex) in tropical countries around the world

k) Canoe Knife
Made by John Wilson, and sold or bartered through the Hudson's Bay Company in Canada. Used in the making of Birch bark canoes

l) Sheep Shears
With incurved bows, one of many different patterns, made by Burgon and Ball, Sheffield, and sold worldwide

m) Kukri
Gurkhas' fighting knife, of which many were made in England during the Second World War

n) Hunting Knife
Long spear point, black horn handle and leather sheath

o) Bowie Knife
Acid etched blade with Clipt point. Stag scales on handle

p) Hunting Knife
Clipt point, acid etched blade. With metal handle

q) Self-defence Knife
Acid etched blade, Clipt point and 'Thorn Dot' handle for secure grip

r) Dagger
Spear point, acid etched blade and stag handle

a

b

c

d

e

f

g

h

i

j

7.49

k

l

o

m

p

q

n

r

7.50

Pile of used pots for Crucible steel melting at Abbeydale Works

One might ask, what is an engineer? There are of course many definitions but all involve an association with machinery, its design, application and maintenance. Today in the 21st Century it is now generally accepted that engineers can be classified within seventeen main trade sectors ranging from aerospace to structural.

Tools in the Ken Hawley Collection cover some, if not all of these trades but nevertheless include a very wide range and diversity of applications, only a few of which can be mentioned here. Cold chisels ranging from ¼″ to 1¼″ in width were made in various flat shapes, cross-cut and half-round for use in fabricating and cutting metal plates, grooving, also removing rivets in association with heavy hammers, particularly in the shipbuilding industry. Use of these tools has declined since 1900 when oxyacetylene cutting and welding was developed and became readily available. Hammers too were made in hundreds of patterns and in weights from 4oz to 21 pounds. These were all sold by weight, and in 1910 this was at a rate of some 7d or 8d per pound, according to the Sheffield Illustrated List.

Hand drills up to ¼″ capacity, breast drills up to ½″ and ratchet braces were all used for producing holes in wood and metal using a variety of drill bits; there was a gradual demise in their use with the introduction of electric powered drills, also CNC machinery, and later laser technology for mass production. Drill bits for a ratchet brace would have been simply flat or twisted steel, with a pointed end and a square shank, forged by blacksmiths. Some were also used as centre bits for wood; these too were flat, with a central point, and two projecting spurs which helped keep the hole true. Another style had diamond shaped points and others were made in rose or snail horn pattern as countersinks, used to recess screw heads. This applied up until the 19th Century when twist drills were invented by Stephen Morse in 1861. His first patent was applied for in 1863 and in 1864 the Morse Twist Drill and Manufacturing Company was formed in America. It is thought that around this time, metal hacksaws and frames started to be utilised for cutting steel rod or bar. Before this time, bowsaws, used in woodworking, were adapted for cutting iron and these were used with blades which could be easily re-sharpened.

Universally used by engineers was a variety of spanners and wrenches, the former in early days of their development were called screw keys and almost invariably had open-ended jaws. Many wrenches were available, from a simple wedge action adjustable wrench with the sliding jaw locked by a metal wedge, to grip or cam action types and screw adjustable wrenches. Handles might be straight or curved to allow easier access for difficult jobs.

Files were one of the most frequently used engineers' tools with thousands of sizes, types and patterns; where Britain led the world there are now no UK file-makers. There are foreign imports but much of the work of removing excess metal is now carried out by powered angle grinders, and the use of modern, more accurate machining techniques.

Tinsmiths' shears and other types of hand shears for sheet metal cutting were usually made with straight or curved blades meeting at a point, and handles which also met at the base of the tool. Pincers and nippers were generally similar but shorter and with an end cutting action. Pliers could be used for gripping but many would also have a facility for cutting wire.

Numerous cramps, including sash, 'G' cramps, bench holdfasts, drilling pillars, used for supporting ratchet braces and several designs of vice were employed to ensure that work was securely held during

Jimping: A milled, ornamental edge to the liners of a pocket knife; also the decorative grinding on the back of an open razor.

Concealed pin: Table knives pinned on to the haft from the choil edge (the cutting edge), without carrying the pins right through to the back edge, or 'mock pinned'.

Notch hollow: A notch in the scale of a pen or pocket knife, where the thumb goes to reach the nail nick to open the blade.

8.51

8.52

a

b

c

d

e

f

g

h

i

j

k

l

m

n

o

p

q

r

s

t

a) Engineers' 'Flogging' Hammer *Weighing four pounds, and with short shaft for striking in confined spaces. Early 20th Century*

b) Engineers' Ball Pein Riveting Hammer *Used in shipbuilding, railway and other allied construction industries. Early 20th Century*

c) Organ Builders' Float *Used for scraping soft metals, tin etc., i.e. organ pipes. c.1900*

d) Valve Rocker File *Specifically used for hand filing of recessed valve faces on steam engines. 19th to mid 20th Century*

e) 'Rubber' File *Used for fettling, (cleaning up) iron castings. 19th Century*

f) Engineers' File *Double-tanged, and made in lengths up to 48" for heavy engineering (two operators), 19th Century*

g) Tramway Track File *For use by two men, using extended handles*

h) Milled Tooth File *Used for heavy duty filing of flat surfaces. Mid 20th Century*

i) Drill Chuck *'Open' pattern, for use on lathes or in pillar drills, Early 20th Century*

j) Lathe Chuck *From an early automatic lathe, and used in Sheffield for bolt and nut making. 19th Century*

k) Bench Vice *A semi-portable vice, made of wrought iron, with steel jaws*

l) Engineers' Bench Vice *The lever action ensures positive tightening, and instantaneous grip of the work-piece. Early 20th Century*

m) Engineers' Bottle Jack *Screw lifting pattern, portable jack. Capable of supporting weights from 1½ to 20 tons. Early 20th Century*

n) Adjustable Spanner *Rack pattern, made in mid 19th Century*

o) Adjustable Spanner *Wedge pattern, early to mid 19th Century*

p) Adjustable Spanner *'Shim' pattern, mid 19th Century*

q) Engineers' Ratchet Brace *Used with drill bit for drilling holes in iron or steel. 19th to early 20th Century*

r) Screw Punching Bear *For making holes in steel or iron plate*

s) Bow Saw *Lancashire pattern (Hacksaw). Used for cutting iron, formerly termed an Iron Bow Saw. Early 19th Century*

t) Bow Saw *Adjustable pattern, late 19th Century (see s) above)*

manufacturing processes.

Another widely used piece of equipment, used for many engineering and blacksmithing applications was the anvil, a large, shaped block of iron, but steel faced. These would have been used by file-cutters, also for sickle making, pen and pocket blade forging as well as the better known blacksmiths and farriers anvils, all of which were exported worldwide from Sheffield. The collection has something in the region of sixty different types of anvil.

Gassing: 4d. or 6d. a week
paid to employers for the use of gas.

Cams for working the overhead vertical blowers in Abbeydale Works Tilt Shop

Saw piercing:
Decorative fretwork designs made by sawing into spoon tops, fish eaters, bowls, dishes etc.

Moit: *A mote in the eye, of steel or stone in particular. Grinders were expert in removing these.*

Huber adjustable spanner with moveable shims to accommodate a variety of nut or component sizes

Pile side: *Reverse side of the blade from the mark side, often shows the cutler's thumb print.*

k) Steel Rule Four-fold pattern. Graduated in notches of varying depth to denote ¼", ½" and 1" increments, and used for measuring by blind operatives. James Chesterman and Co. 20th Century

l) Printing Gauge Folding gauge with six scale arms and type sizes graduated in 'points'. Marked with the Monotype name, it was probably used by operators of hot metal typesetting machines, to check sizing and page fitting

m) Steel Rule Folding, pocket size metal rule, graduated in Russian 'inches' by the reverse etch process. James Chesterman and Co. Mid.19th Century

n) Boxwood Folding Rule 20" in length, two fold and graduated in inches and tenths of an inch. Marked Joseph Whitworth, Manchester, and made by John Rabone, Birmingham. Late 19th Century

o) Boxwood Folding Rule 24" in length, two fold, Routledge pattern for engineers. Faces are marked with several tables of constants. One arm features a sliding brass logarithmic scale and protractor. John Rabone, late 19th Century

a) Spirit Level Horsfalls patent. Used when levelling line-shafting for belt drives, complete with instruction board. Late 19th Century

b) Micrometer 'Direct Reading' 0 to 2". Machined, cast bronze frame and 3-point anvil. Used for measuring thickness of glass and lead sheet. Readout on drum is in ounces per square foot for glass and pounds per square foot for lead. Exhibited at the Great Exhibition 1851 by Hayward of London

c) Micrometer Range, 0 to ¼". Solid cast bronze frame, and used for measuring cold rolled strip at James Chesterman's works, but made in the USA. Early 20th Century

d) Micrometer Range, 0 to 2". Graduated in 1/1000". The frame is wrought iron with drum and screw action, together with an external fiducial line. Thought to have been made late 18th early 19th Century. No makers mark

e) Braille Micrometer Range, 0 to 1". A unique gauge used by blind inspectors for engineering components. Designed and made by Moore and Wright, Sheffield. Mid 20th Century

f) Micrometer or 'Linemeter' Range, 0 to 3". Cast in brass with square 'bow'. Used for the accurate measurement of test specimens in 1/1000". Made by H.J.H. King, Glasgow, late 19th Century

g) Vernier Calliper Gauge 24" capacity and reading in 1/1000". The instrument is reputed to be the first gauge of this pattern and was made by James Chesterman and Co in 1910, after buying a Screw Dividing Machine from Société Genevoise in Switzerland. This was the only machine capable of dividing gauge scales to this accuracy, and the actual machine now forms part of the Ken Hawley Collection

h) Vernier Calliper Gauge Continental pattern, to measure up to 500mm. Equipped with straight jaws on one side which enables both internal and external measurement. The opposite side has a pair of calliper pattern jaws. Probably German, early 20th Century

i) Taper Gauge Wood mounted gauge for checking measurement of test pieces using a pair of callipers. Reading is taken at the point of contact. James Chesterman, early 20th Century

j) Wire Gauge Hardened steel gauge, used for measuring 1 to 36 Birmingham Wire Gauges. Made by P. Stubs for James Chesterman, it is intaglio etched in script with the owners' name, also that of J. Bingham, user. Mid 19th Century

8.54

a

b

c

d

e

f

g

h

i

j

k

l

8.55

m

n

o

Ken Hawley demonstrating hand file cutting, using a lead bed and leather straps to secure the file blank. Note the leather shoe, used as a hammer holder

Most of the tools in this section were tools used in the process of removing excess material or the production of holes in a range of metals from copper or aluminium through to stainless steel. Their efficacy depended on their property of being harder and more durable than the materials they were designed to cut.

Earliest hardened steels date back to 1200 BC in China, and 'Wootz' steel made in India around 350 BC. These were followed much later in 540 AD and 900 AD by Damascus and Japanese layered type steel. After Huntsmans' discovery of crucible cast steel circa 1740, in 1869 Robert Forester Mushet, developed a steel which was the forerunner of high speed steels. This consisted of 2% Carbon, 2.5% Manganese, and 7% Wolfram (Tungsten). Later developments meant that Manganese was superseded by another element, Chromium. The main property of this new steel was that it hardened considerably when allowed to cool in air. At the turn of the 20th Century, Mushet steel was used at the Bethlehem Steel Co in Pennsylvania for a series of heat treatment experiments carried out by two engineers, Frederick Winslow Taylor, and Maunsell White. As a result of these experiments and subsequent testing, these proved beyond doubt that these steels could retain their hardness at the cutting edge far in excess of plain carbon steels, thus dramatically reducing the time needed to machine components, and so, modern high speed steel was born.

Simple forms of lathes have been dated to 700 BC but it was not until Jacques de Vaucanson invented the first slide lathe for cylindrical turning in 1751, followed in 1797 by Henry Maudslay's screw cutting lathe meant that this form of metal cutting came into use. Consequently, tools for these were one of the earliest cutting tools and similar tools would have been used in slotting and shaping machines where by a reciprocating action, thin slivers of metal could be removed even on curved shapes. Planing machines used similar shaped tools, and from the early 20th Century some of these were butt-welded to mild steel to reduce costs. Twist drills were another relatively early tool, first with straight shanks until development of the Morse taper shank which was a friction fit and didn't slip in the holding device. These taper steel drills were also butt-welded between the end of the flutes and the shank. Many designs of twist drill evolved with the angle of the helix ranging from quick to slow for different materials. Also the point angle could be varied to achieve an optimum cut. One interesting twist drill was the FBT 'Speedicut' Chipbreaker drill with a special rib milled into the shape of the flute to divert and break the metal swarf spiralling off the component. The Ken Hawley Collection has the original development tools and the special flute cutters used in their production. Drills normally produce a true hole in metal components but often the finish is required to be smoother and more accurate. This is achieved by the use of a reamer which has more and shallower flutes which have a less steep helix angle to give a planing or shearing action.

Taps and dies for producing both external and internal screw threads date from the late 18th Century, and these covered the basic thread forms of

Grinder's asthma:
Tuberculosis, caused by breathing in fine dust from stone and metal produced by grinding.

Cuckoos: *Faulty work, sent back to be put right.*

Poking: *Being forced to take work to another grinding shop, or borrow room to work.*

9.57

Firth Brown Tools prototype Chipbreaker drill, showing milled rib for breaking chips

9.58

a) Face Milling Cutter *Made in carbon steel. Fine pitch teeth. 19th Century*

b) 'Gang Cutter' *One of a series of vee toothed 'gang cutters', used for toothing machine knives. 19th Century*

c) Slotting Cutter *Well worn and much sharpened early carbon steel cutter from Brown & Sharpe. 19th Century*

d) Slitting Cutter *Carbon steel, 'Tradesman' made, with ground teeth*

e) Lathe Tool *A 'spring' tool for turning metal components which will enable light finishing cuts. c.19th Century*

f) Flat Drill *Made with a diamond point from an old file blade and used in a lathe. The lathe tailstock produced horizontal feed. 19th Century*

g) Lathe Boring Tool *Blacksmith forged from Earl Fitzwilliam's estate. Made during WW1. Some war work was done and contributed by landowners. Marked E.F.W., early 20th Century*

h) Set of Lathe Tools *Model Engineers' Patent pattern. Tools in set are for screw-cutting, parting-off and boring, complete with adjustment key. Sold by S. Tyzack & Sons, London c.1930's*

i) Morse Taper Shank Twist Drill *Made of high speed steel with a blue, thermal (dry steam), finish, and used for drilling armour plate. 20th Century*

j) Ratchet Shank Twist Drill *No.2 size shank and made from carbon steel, for use in an Engineers' Ratchet Brace*

k) Morse Taper Shank Twist Drill *Made of high speed steel, the gold colour finish is a Titanium Nitride coating, developed in the late 20th Century to provide low friction cutting and a longer tool life when drilling modern materials*

l) Twist Drill *This 'experimental' example was made by twisting a flat bar to provide the spiral flutes, with a Morse taper shank and an ejection tang. Sheffield, early 20th Century*

m) Combined Drill Reamer *A combination tool, part drill, part reamer to produce an accurate hole size and a superior finish in one pass, rather than using separate tools. Mid 20th Century*

n) Adjustable Hand Reamer *With straight, high speed steel cutting blades, and a sliding extension collar. Formerly used for renovating automobile steering arm bushes, but now outdated. From mid 20th Century*

Whitworth, BA, BS Pipe, Unified and Metric, each developed over a period of time to suit many industrial applications. In early days these were made from carbon rather than high speed steel. These tools were used in various designs of die-stocks or tap wrenches when used by hand.

Moving on to the 20th Century, powder metallurgy came into being from work done in Germany in 1927, and this technology was first taken up in Sheffield by Firth Brown Tools and sold under the 'Mitia' brand of tungsten carbide.

Not to be forgotten are some of the heaviest cutting tools such as milling cutters, also segmented cutters and saws, and circular saws. These were all used for machining large components, many being used in the motor and other engineering industries.

Pike:

The beck, or pointed end of an anvil.

9.59

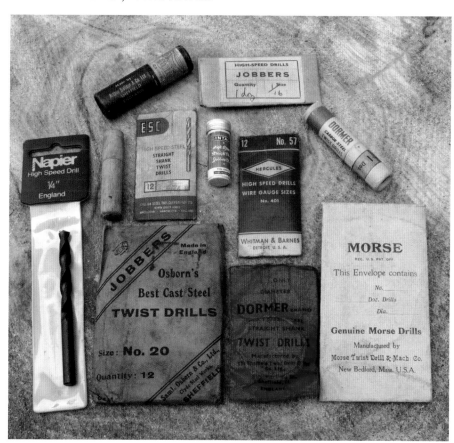

Twist Drill packaging

o) Ratchet Drills *Two examples of carbon steel drills with diamond points, forged in Sheffield for 'on site' use in constructional steelwork and similar applications, c.19th Century*

Scale tang: Tang of a table or butchers' knife, to which two scales are fastened.

An adjustable screw plate, used for cutting external threads

Witch: A tool used by spring knife cutlers to stop scales bending, whilst being riveted.

a) Adjustable Diestock
Whitworth patented pattern. This uses three chasers to cut the threads on bar materials. Mid-late 19th Century

b) Adjustable Diestock
Patented pattern, with twin split dies for cutting the thread form. 19th Century

c) Tap Wrench
Three hole pattern, Blacksmith forged in wrought iron. Early design from 18th Century

d), e) Engineers' Screw Taps
Blacksmith forged and used to produce screw holes in wrought iron only. Taps are tapered for the full thread length, probably to allow for the crudely cut hole sizes of the period. 18th to 19th Century

f) Master Tap
2 ¾" Whitworth thread form. Used for making dies or other screw-cutting tools. G & J Hall, 19th-20th Century

g) Master Tap
5" British Standard Pipe thread form (approx 5 ½" diameter). Used as f). 19th -20th Century

h, i, j, k) Hand Taps
British Standard Gas thread form. With drills combined, these were designed to produce internal threads for water, gas or similar pipes under pressure, using a hand operated Ratchet Drill. k) Also has a built-in seating cutter

l, m, n, o, p) Screw Plates
Used for cutting external screw threads, there are many different patterns but both plain and adjustable types are illustrated. n) for example, is capable of producing threads of 14 different diameters. Mid 19th Century

q) Hand Chaser
External pattern thread chaser, for hand cutting screw threads using a lathe

a

b

c

d

e

f

g

h

i

j

k

l

m

n

o

p

q

9.61

10.62

Sheffield built its world famous reputation for cutlery over a period of perhaps 900 years or so, and the first authenticated record of a cutler in the town, dates back to 1297 AD. Another proven record is from 1340 AD when an inventory of King Edward lll's possessions was taken in the Tower of London, and mentioned in his will was a knife which had been made in Sheffield.

In the true sense of the word, cutlery 'cuts', and this terminology was applied strictly to knives in the very early days. Forks and spoons however were always referred to as flatware. Indeed, forks as an item of tableware, did not appear until the 17th Century, the first examples coming originally from Italy. They were somewhat crude, as they were at that time, forged from iron or steel by blacksmiths. From the early 19th Century an alloy of nickel silver, which was easily formed, was developed and extensively used for spoon and fork manufacture. It was later found that this material could also be electro plated with silver and the term EPNS was coined. This was a rust free product and silver being an inert material, meant no

O'er cutting: Most files are double-cut; the o'ercutting is the first cut, and this is crossed by the second 'up' cut.

Little mester: A master cutler working on his own, but in a rented factory room; he would deal through a factor to sell his goods.

Whetstone: A slab of Brincliffe stone. Warehouse women used to swish the knife edge quickly along the stone to produce a keen cutting edge.

metal 'after taste' when eating. As mentioned in an earlier chapter, Henry Brearley was experimenting with metal alloys from around 1908 and in 1913 he made the first true, what was at that time, rust-less steel, later renamed stainless steel. Several cutlers were asked to try this but had a number of manufacturing difficulties until R.F. Mosley became the first firm of cutlers to adopt stainless steel for table knives.

From old catalogues there appeared to be countless designs for table knives and forks and around 1816 knife-blades were much longer and larger than today with basic shapes having mostly rounded but some with more pointed ends. Large blades meant that such foodstuffs as peas and gravy could be scooped up from the plate, and several different blade lengths were available.

Some knives had round tangs which could be easily fixed into bone handles. Others had scale tangs allowing various woods, also horn, ivory, tortoiseshell etc., to be pinned or riveted on each side of the tang to form a handle. Horn, usually buffalo, first needed to be

a) Cased Cutlery Set
Set of twelve, 'close' plated dessert knives, with ivory handles and silver ferrules, in wooden case. Mid 19th Century

b) Cased Cutlery Set
Containing six each fish eaters (knives), and forks, all with pearl handles and silver ferrules. Early 20th Century

c) Ladies Manicure Set
Wooden, cased set of ladies manicure instruments, some with Mother of Pearl, others with Tortoiseshell handles. Made in Sheffield in the 1930's

d) Sports Trophy
Made in E.P.N.S., for The Sheffield Twist Drill and Steel Company Ltd., and competed for in events after WW2

e) Candlestick
Sterling Silver, stamped in steel dies, then soldered together. Maker, Walker and Hall, Sheffield 1923 Hallmark

f) Candlestick
Also in Sterling Silver, but hand raised and fluted from sheet silver, by Wallace Smythe, Sheffield 1953 Hallmark

g) Sauce Boat
One of the unique and very interesting items in the Collection is this Sterling Silver Sauce Boat. It was hand raised and fluted by Ken Hawley himself, under the tutelage of Wallace Smythe, designer at Mappin and Webb, Sheffield, in order to learn and understand more of the skills and manufacturing secrets used in the hollow-ware trades. 1953 Hallmark

h) Fruit Bowl
Sterling Silver, using technique of saw piercing the vine pattern by Bill Thornton 1973

i, j) Military Swords
One sword has its original leather scabbard. Both have acid etched designs on both sides of the blades. Each has a simple metal basket guard with shagreen and wire bound handles. Made by Clement Gray, Sheffield in 1930's

k) City & Guilds Test Piece
A wood mounted, engraved brass test piece, produced for City & Guilds examination by engraver Willie Kugler, Sheffield, early 20th Century

10.63

made pliable by heating in oil before being pressed in steel dies, tortoiseshell also lending itself to pressing. All these materials could be further embellished by filing or with incised chequering in other geometric or ornamental patterns. In EPNS and stainless cutlery and flatware a standard range of 'parish patterns', Kings, Queens, Shell, Bead, Fiddle etc. were also developed and are still used today. We should not forget the late David Mellor a Sheffield silversmith who produced twenty seven designs of cutlery including 'Pride' in 1963 which is silver plated and dishwasher proof. He was a Royal designer and in 1971 he re-designed two 'Eclipse' metal-cutting saws for James Neill Tools.

Silver-smithing was another early trade to develop in Sheffield from the early 18th Century. It was around this time, in 1742 when Thomas Bolsover (sometimes spelled Boulsover), accidentally discovered when heating a knife handle made of copper and silver, that the two metals fused together, the lower melting point silver flowing as a very thin layer and bonding to the copper. This later became known as Old Sheffield Plate. Bolsover himself only used this material for small items like snuffboxes, knife handles and the like but others developed the process so that hollowware like tureens, tankards, trays and bowls and also candlesticks could be made. Old Sheffield Plate was stronger and much cheaper than solid silver but edges showing the copper

Tines: Prongs or points of any instrument.

Lood wark: Work not completed on time.

layer had to be disguised by the addition of decorative silver wire or thin rolled strip being soldered into place.

There were a number of methods of embellishing articles of silverware or Old Sheffield Plate, the first of these was engraving when a design would have been cut or incised into the metal. In the case of Old Sheffield Plate, this was not possible unless a thicker layer of silver was used to avoid cutting into and exposing the copper. Chasing or Repoussé was the process of producing relief designs by deforming the metal. This delicate work was achieved using special hammers, small sharpened chisels and a range of punches; being labour intensive this was usually found on more expensive items of silverware. Similar craftsmanship and time was needed for saw-piercing and this could produce an incredible variety of delicate filigree work. Intricate designs were made possible by the use of paper or thin brass patterns and tiny holes would be pierced in the areas of metal to be removed. Then, very fine saw blades were threaded through the holes and by using a large piercing saw, even very difficult to access parts of almost any object could be cut out to reproduce a decorative pattern. As improved methods were developed, die-sinkers were able to produce complicated designs for large metal punches which could then be stamped into the work, forming a relief image.

a) Bread Knife *Shear steel blade, ivory handle carved with 'corn on the cob' design, representing 'plenty'. Late 19th Century*

b) Dessert Knife and Fork *Engraved, and with electroplated blades and coloured porcelain handles, c.1880*

c) Table Knife and Fork *Humped scimitar pattern shear steel blade, and fork with two tines. Stamped pistol pattern handles. Late 18th Century*

d)' Pic-nic' Set *Slot pattern, carbon steel knife, corkscrew and fork, also sterling silver spoon. Ivory handle scales. Maker John Nowill, late 18th Century*

e) Caviar Knife *Made of Mother of Pearl (metal blade would taint the caviar). Sheffield maker, W.Gillot & Son. Late 20th Century*

f) Afternoon Tea Spoon *Mother of Pearl and made by W. Gillot as above*

g) Fruit Knife *Sterling silver blade, Mother of Pearl scales, diamond cut with silver studs. Late 19th Century*

h) Table Knife *Humped scimitar pattern shear steel blade, with green stained ivory handle, silver ferrule and French cap. Late 18th Century*

i) 'Lunatic' Knife *Round point with only 1" of cutting edge. Horn handle scales. Used by asylum inmates in the late 19th Century who might harm themselves or others. Made by John Petty, Sheffield*

j) Table Knife *Stainless steel blade, acid etched with armorial device and makers name R F Moseley. Carved ivory handle. (This company was the world's first maker of stainless steel cutlery in the 1930's)*

k) Meat Carvers *(Knife, fork and steel, set of three in leather case) With double shear steel blades, spear point and palette neck. Sambar horn handles, silver ferrules and cap. Fork has Jos. Rodgers patent swivel guard. Late 19th Century*

l) Masticating Knife and Fork Set *Knife has three parallel detachable blades for cutting food into tiny pieces, and useful for people without teeth. Ivory handles. Made by Jos. Rodgers late 19th Century*

m) 'Nelson' or Amputees Knife *Blade is made of shear steel with 'fork' on back edge. Ivory handled. This item can be traced back to a user who is thought to have lost an arm in a saw mill accident. Mid 19th Century*

n) Fish Slice *Close plated nickel silver, and saw pierced. Mid 19th Century*

o) Fish Eaters *E.P.N.S. blades and carved ivory handles with silver ferrules. End 20th Century*

a

b

c

d

e

f

g

h

i

j

k

l

m

n

o

10.65

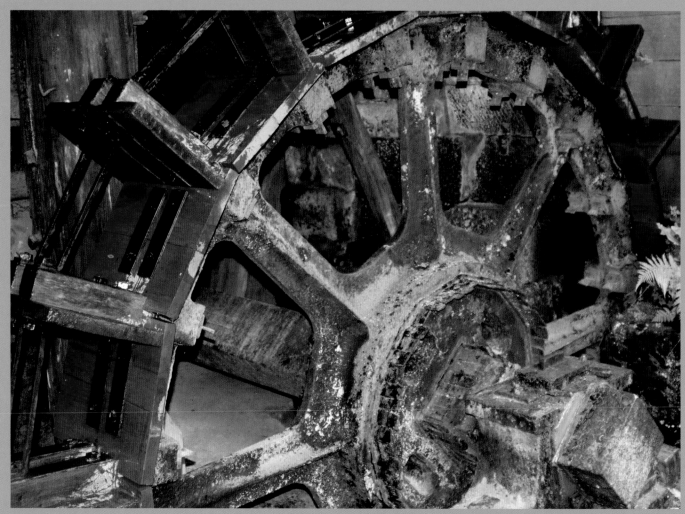

One of the waterwheels at Wortley Top Forge

This section includes certain knives not mentioned elsewhere including pen and pocket knives, razors, scissors, domestic tools and household implements. In the era of the famous 19th Century cook Mrs Beeton, before the introduction of rotary hand mincing machines and hand or electric powered shredders, many herbs, vegetables and other produce were reduced to manageable size by the use of hand mincing knives made from saw plate, with a flat or curved edge, depending on whether they were used on a flat wooden board or in a bowl. Carrot knives were of a serrated section, allowing carrots to be chopped with a more interesting crinkle shape.

Some of the households' domestic tools might have included meat choppers for trimming large joints of meat as we were, by and large, a nation of meat eaters. Sugar choppers were an essential tool, as sugar was supplied in large solid cones, not granulated as today. Chunks of sugar which had been chopped off were then broken into smaller lumps by sugar nippers, ready for table use. A Champagne nipper had a side cutting tool to sever wires, also a serrated handle end for prising up corks, the other handle was furnished with a small stiff brush for removing cellar dirt from the cork. Wine and other drinks were popular, and tools such as awl-like ice picks for breaking up ice from the family

Whet: *To sharpen knives or tools.*

ice-house, wine waiters knives, corkscrews with wood, metal or bone handles and crown cork openers came in many designs. Nutcrackers too and tin openers were made in a variety of types.

An interesting tool was the cucumber slicer which was essentially a flat piece of steel with a nickel plated blade secured with adjustable springs and screws. The cucumber was moved across this to provide regular even slices. Mechanical egg beaters superseded egg whisks for easier mixing. Other tools might include pokers, fire shovels and coal hammers – these would generally have the word 'coal'

Owe: *To re-surface a grinding wheel, by hacking with a special chisel-edged hammer.*

cast into the head. Beds were made of heavy wood frames with metal-linked springing and these were bolted together by use of open ended 'Bed-Keys'.

Other associated domestic items might include bread boards, also made in Sheffield, toasting forks, cooks forks, button hooks and needles in a vast range of sizes. A new addition to the collection is a rather strange tool used by beekeepers. This was a spur embedding tool, with a revolving, serrated gear wheel made of brass, into which a 'V' had been cut in the teeth. The tool had a bulbous 'heatsink' and when heated over a flame, was used to embed support wires into a beeswax foundation which the bees later drew out into the comb. (see illustration on page 70.)

Pen knives, as the name perhaps

11.67

Miniature razor and pocket knife with 5p coin, 18mm diameter for scale

implies, were made initially to sharpen quill pens which had been used from around the 7th Century onwards. Early examples were in the form of a small sharp blade, fixed into the end of a handle, and used to keep the writing implement of the home or office, trimmed and sharp. Later, although 'folding' knives had been around since Roman times, the first spring penknife was developed in the 16th Century. The blade(s) of this were through pinned to the handle by means of a 'joint'. This allowed blades to fold into the handle so that the knife could be safely carried in a pocket or ladies handbag and such knives were often of quite delicate design.

Nickerpecker:
Nickname for hand file cutters; their hammering was likened to the sound of woodpeckers.

Beard: *A very short bolster, a sort of rounded half-bolster; the tip of a knife haft.*

A pocket knife was essentially a workman's tool, with a spring or shut design for pocket use. They were much larger, with stronger blades and used by anyone who needed a general purpose knife for gardening, pruning and similar tasks, certainly all farmers and countrymen carried a knife by rote. Since the near demise of Sheffield's pocket knife industry, its place has been taken by the ubiquitous Stanley knife, which was not originally designed for pocket use.

Perhaps considered a 'man only' item of cutlery was the old 'open' or 'cut throat' razor for shaving, and Sheffield was noted for the quality and sometimes beautiful decoration of the blades, also the scales and handles. The Collection houses many

different designs of these but also has another example, termed a harem razor. Open razors started to become obsolete after 1904 when King C. Gillette patented probably the first double-edged safety razor, and by the end of the 1920's Sheffield was producing countless quantities of what was known as a 3-hole or wafer blade. By the1960's many changes were taking place as plastic moulded handles were introduced, and these razors carried 2, 3, 4 and later five blades and were 'disposable'. This meant the demise of the 19th Century Sheffield razor forgers, grinders and handle makers, who used carved ivory, mother-of-pearl and

Ivory Pen Machine, for cutting nibs on quill pens

a) Set of Twelve Razors
This set of twelve razors was made in Sheffield by John Heifor, probably for the Great Exhibition of 1851. They are unique and of exquisite design and workmanship, using exotic materials for handles, such as Mother of Pearl, Tortoiseshell, Ivory, Rosewood and Stag's Horn. Some are stained, others pierced, engraved or carved or inset with a different material

b) '7-Day' Razor Set
This cased '7 day' set of ivory handled razors was made c.1900 by Jos. Rodgers, Sheffield. Each razor is acid etched with the day of the week, to be used on that day only. This ensured that the razors were 'rested' for a week to allow the blade to recover its deformed edge after shaving

c) Razor
A Geo. Wostenholme razor with a most exquisite acid etched blade. This, together with the perfect grinding and polishing, produced a razor worthy of being classed as Fine Art. Tortoiseshell handle, c.1900

d) Razor
A common design with the scales made from pressed grey buffalo horn, featuring a man with a gun and his dog. The method was to cut the design into a steel die, into which the horn was pressed after heating in oil. Even the buttons on the man's gaiters, can be seen clearly. Made c.1840

e) Tailors' Cutting Out Shears
These shears are lined with crucible cast steel, and have cast brass handles, c.1900

f) Bankers Scissors
Blades are some 12" in length. Made by Jos. Rodgers, Sheffield

g) Scissors
A selection of five hard polished scissors of fine workmanship which has never been bettered. The hand filed shanks and bows are delicately formed and crafted. They include (l to r), Buttonhole, Embroidery, Unknown, but with sharp-pointed blades, curved in two planes, Dressmakers and Embroidery

h) Scissors
Scimitar pattern blades, designed possibly for Eastern European markets. Maker, John Nowill

i) Scissors
Persian pattern, and used by women in the manufacture of their country's carpets. The design is also thought to allow their use as a dagger in an emergency. Made c.1900

a

11.69

b

c

d

e

f

g

h

i

tortoiseshell to enhance the product.

Scissors were, and still remain the only piece of cutlery where two blades work in opposition to one another, by means of a pinned joint, in order to cut thin material such as paper, cloth and even thin metals. Again the heyday of the Sheffield scissor trade was in the 19th Century when its craftsmen created some incredible works of art, with ladies embroidery scissors being the most decorative. There were scissors for dressmaking, buttonholing, tailoring, fingernails and cuticles with straight or bent blades, even flower gathering scissors which held blooms as they were cut, so as not to fall on the ground. Kitchen scissors were an all-purpose tool with heavy blades which could be generally abused and still cut food like wet fish, as one blade was serrated. Other gadgets were often designed into kitchen scissors such as tin and bottle openers. How many modern homes have a range of scissors anymore?

Pistol haft: *A common type of pocket knife with a haft resembling the butt of an old-fashioned pistol.*

11.70

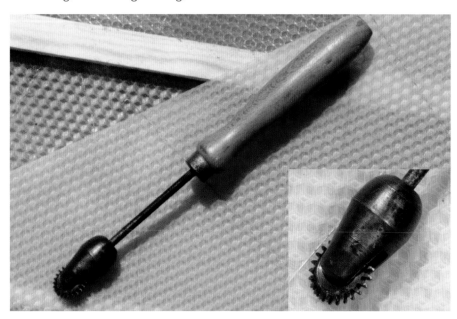

Beekeepers' Spur Embedding Tool for hot moulding pre-formed beeswax sheet onto support wires

a) Sportsmans' Knife *Fitted with 'pocket' blade, corkscrew, champagne hook, button hook and cartridge extractor. Nickel silver scales, and made by Jos. Rodgers c.1900*

b) Pocket Knife *Broad spear blade with Sambar stag horn scales. Marked, J Heffor, Sheffield, mid 19th Century*

c) Pocket Knife *Blade with Clipt point, featuring a hunting scene. Stag horn scales. Maker, J Wostenholme, early 19th Century*

d) Pistol Knife *Spear point blade and Black Buffalo horn scales, diamond cut. Maker Unwin and Rodgers, mid 19th Century*

e) Sportsmans' Knife *Two blades, plus nine 'articles' for different uses, (the ninth is a turnscrew end to a middle scale). An exhibition quality knife made by Jos. Wostenholme in the late 19th Century*

f) Box Knife *Broad spear and pen spear blades, hand cut nail file, snuff box with hinged lid. Ivory and Tortoiseshell scales with 'let-in'. No makers name, Sheffield, early 19th Century*

g) Pen Machine *For quill pens, the art of pen nibbing was assisted by the invention of this machine. This had a sliding blade, a punch and die to form the quill end and a tiny blade to cut the ink drain together with a guillotine to trim and angle the point for right or left hand users. Housed in Ebony handle and made by Jos. Rodgers, early 19th Century*

h) Pen Knife *Spring action blade, which most users associate with the name 'penknife'. Ivory scales, with tiny silver studs in a flower pattern, and fluted edges. Sheffield made with London cutlery shop name. Almost certainly sold as a ladies gift. 19th Century*

i) Pen Knife *This original pen knife is a fine blade fixed in the end of an Ivory handle. This was used solely for cutting the end of a wing feather (the quill), of a female Swan or Pen (hence the name) to shape, in order to write with. Sheffield 18th –19th Century*

j) Pen Knife *Single bladed. Also used as a propelling pencil, in flintlock gun pattern. Jos. Rodgers, Sheffield 19th Century*

k) Knife Scissors *Two 'pen' blades and pair of scissors, with Tortoiseshell scales. When new, these would be supplied with a protective case, formed of paper, similar to a razor case. Made c.1800*

a

b

c

d

e

f

g

h

i

j

k

l

m

n

o

a) **Coal Hammer** *Marked 'Coal' and used in Victorian households for breaking up large lumps of coal to put on the fire. Early 20th Century*

b) **Button Hook** *A portable 'help' tool; used to fasten ladies glove buttons. 19th to early 20th Century*

c) **Bed Key** *Of many types and patterns; a three arm spanner for different nut sizes, used to tighten springs of Victorian beds. 19th to early 20th Century*

d) **Cucumber Slicer** *This kitchen utensil is unfortunately minus its blade, but is made from Mahogany and Brass, and probably not very hygienic. Made in Sheffield, 19th Century*

e) **Ice Skate** *In the mid 19th Century, Sheffield was famous for its ice skate blades. This example was made as part of an exhibit for the 1851 Great Exhibition and is in Rosewood inlaid with nickel silver emblems of the Scottish Thistle and an Irish Clover leaf, together with a decorative star. The blade is made of crucible cast steel.*

f) **Mincing Knife** *For chopping food ingredients, into small pieces using a bowl. This handle is reminiscent of a saw handle, but much more ornate. There are many other patterns, some equipped with rectangular blades. 19th Century*

g) **Corkscrew and Brush** *With bone handle, and used for opening wine bottles by a butler. The brush is to remove any dust that may have gathered on the bottle whilst in the cellar. Mid 19th Century*

h) **Vegetable Slicer** *A wooden handled cheap kitchen knife. Supplied with a guard to make vegetable slicing safer and easier. c.1900*

i) **Corkscrew** *A metal corkscrew which folds into its handle for carrying in the pocket. These were a common item in Victorian times. 19th Century*

j) **Nutmeg Grater** *A steel blade, rasp cut on both sides, to produce fine or coarse nutmeg for adding to the top of rice puddings*

k) **Tin Opener** *Handle is of cast iron, in shape of bulls head and tail. Steel blade and used for opening 'Bully Beef' tins*

l) **Tin Opener** *Cast in the shape of a fish, and used for opening sardine tins*

m) **Sugar Chopper** *Cast steel blade with hardwood handle and brass ferrule. Used for rough chopping a 'sugar loaf' into large lumps*

n) **Sugar Tongs** *With spring action and curved jaws, for breaking up the large lumps of sugar to a size suitable for the table*

o) **Ebony Tool Pad** *This unusual set of tools comprised rasps and files, 'turnscrews', chisels and gouges, wood boring tools, a tack claw and others, to form a 24-piece 19th Century 'DIY tool kit*

Apart from tradesmen's tools which are referred to elsewhere in this book, it is not generally known that Sheffield was a centre which developed countless tools and instruments for the medical and veterinary professions. The making of these products employed many people from diverse trades which included hand forgers, grinders, surgical instrument fitters and many others. More specific examples were saw makers making the blades for amputation saws, file-cutters producing bone rasps and files, also iron and brass founders who made castings for a wide range of handles and other components. Razor grinders adapted their skills producing hollow-ground razors for shaving, to a straight, flat-bladed knife used in a mechanical microtome. These were used by microscopists to cut sections of wax-embedded animal or plant tissue as thin as $5-10\ \mu m$ (microns) for study purposes. In comparison, human hair averages about $80\ \mu m$ in diameter.

Rat-tailed file: A 4 or 5 inch slender round file.

Fash: Any rough turned edge caused by filing, or a metal protrusion produced in manufacturing.

Clout nail: Nail with a large flat head, used for nailing leather on to the wooden drum.

The variation in instruments was immense as may be seen in Arnold & Sons catalogue of 1895 consisting of 846 pages – this catalogue features in the collection, which also has many examples of work in progress as well as complete instruments.

Saws included post mortem, amputation, metacarpal and finger patterns, also hand trephines for boring holes in the skull! At least fifty styles of scalpels (knives) including grafting, cataract, cartilage and fistula are listed as standard also a variety of chisels and gouges. Even forceps or tweezers make a total of ninety-two specific designs. Speculae were developed to fit every orifice of the human body for examination purposes and to allow other instruments to be inserted. There are also bullet extractors, tonsil extractors, the list is endless; technology too has changed with lasers and plasma cutting of tissue now becoming a rapidly growing area of development. However, scalpels, many with replaceable blades, were, and are still made in Sheffield by Swann-Morton Ltd., the largest and most modern factory in the world for these products. This company produces 280 million blades annually, in a wide variety of shapes and sizes. (figures from 2010)

The last hand forger in Sheffield is Peter Goss working in a small forge within Kelham Island Museum, tailoring standard instruments to specific dimensions for surgeons. Many people view surgical

12.74

a *b* *c* *d* *e* *f* *g* *h* *i* *j* *k* *l* *m* *n* *o* *p*

Dr. HAGEDORN'S
FLAT SURGEONS' NEEDLES.
THREE-EIGHTHS CIRCLE CURVED.

Dr. HAGEDORN'S
Flat Surgeons' Needles,
QUARTER CIRCLE CURVED.

a) Post Mortem Set *Incomplete set of eight instruments (from 11), in mahogany case. Probably for personal use by a pathologist who might travel to different areas to carry out post mortems*

b) Metacarpel Saw *A compact saw for amputation of fingers. Ivory handle which is randed (bordered), and a diamond cut pattern*

c) Dilator *A three-bladed instrument with a chequered 'eightsquare' Ivory handle. Used for female urethral examinations*

d) Jaw Saw *Small serrated blade of carbon steel fitted with adjustable depth stop. Fluted handle of nickel silver*

e) Thompson's Lithotrite *Made of nickel silver, with fenestrated blade and control wheel, and used for gripping and crushing stones in the bladder or urogenital tract, which were common in Victorian times*

f) Bone Drill *Constructed mainly of brass, the crank is fitted with a wooden handle and provides the drilling action through a bevel gear mechanism. The drills would have been flat and with diamond points*

g) Vaginal Speculum *4-bladed Allingham's pattern, used for female internal genito-urinary examinations*

h) Bullet Extractor *Made of steel, but with brass control handles, and used for extracting bullets from deep in the body through the entry wound*

i) Chain Écraseur *Charrier's pattern with a diamond cut Ebony handle. This crushing instrument used a small metal chain which was looped around tumours, polyps or haemorrhoids, and when pulled very tight around the base or pedicle, crushed or severed this with less bleeding than surgery*

j) Surgical Needles *Packs of needles, of which there were many sizes and patterns. These packets are marked Dr Hagedorn's*

k) Tenotomy Knives *Fisher's pattern, in a set of three. Complete in a leather case, together with a probe. Square section Ivory handles. Maker Down Bros*

instruments with horror, but it must be remembered that they are all designed to help those of us with diseases and deformities to improve expectation of life.

Veterinary instruments are in many cases very similar to those used in surgery on the human body, the main difference being, they were usually larger, particularly for bovine and equine animals. Although essentially, animals had similar functioning organs to humans, their quadruped structure meant that many special tools/

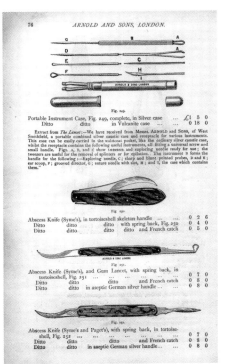
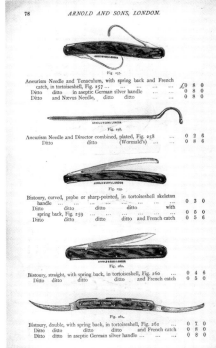

Facsimile pages from Arnold and Sons 1913 catalogue. These illustrate some surgeon's and doctor's instruments for emergency use

l) Guillotine *This instrument operates on a scissor bow system, which on closing, operates the 'D' shaped blade. Its purpose is not exactly known but it may possibly have been used for tonsil's, uvula's or perhaps other oral growths*

m) Bone Cutting Forceps *Original use unknown, but possibly for cutting small bone growths*

n) Shears *Bright nickel plated finish with bow action and probe point. Use unknown*

o) Forceps *With toothed points, this instrument could be used for removal of wound debris, or for dressing wounds*

p) Dissecting Set *A set of seven basic dissecting instruments in a mahogany case, as used by University students*

NB. *Except for the post mortem set, all these instruments were made by J Turton, Sheffield, in the 19th Century. Many were sent to London to be sold through other 'manufacturers'. This trade represented the ultimate in ingenuity and finish, providing surgeons' with instruments for saving countless lives worldwide. Hand-made surgical instruments are still manufactured in Sheffield in 2011. (see also page 78)*

All the above examples were made of carbon steel (pre-stainless), and would rust of course. Handles might be made from Ebony, Ivory, Tortoiseshell and other materials, before the introduction of aseptic handles, made of materials which could be sterilised.

a

b

c

d

e

f

g

h

i

j

k

l

m

n

a) Castrator *This cumbersome instrument would conceivably be used for castrating a large animal like a bull by crushing or severing the sperm ducts. 20th Century*

b) Ear Pliers *Ears of sheep were punched with a hole or mark with this tool for identification purposes. 19th - 20th Century*

c) Tail Docking Shears *Used to shorten the length of an animals' tail by severing the tail bone; but now illegal in the 20th Century. Dates from 19th Century*

d) Hoof Paring Shears *For hoof (toenail), cutting of hoofed animals. 19th Century*

e) Horse Measure *Used for measuring the height of a horse in 'hands,' (one hand equals 4"). The graduated rule is combined within a walking stick, extends from the handle, and retracts when not in use. Made by J Rabone, Birmingham, 19th Century*

f) Castrating Clams *Used for various farm animals. Used as (a) above. 18th-19th Century*

g) Horse Mouth Rasp *Used to rasp down or shorten the front teeth of an older horse. This enables the back teeth to meet, and grind corn or other feedstuffs to a digestible size. 19th - 20th Century*

h) Horse Rasp *This tool is cut on four faces with both rasp and file cut, and enables a farrier to closely fit a shoe on a horse without causing discomfort. 19th - 20th Century*

i) Pig Ring Pliers *Designed to clip an open ring into a pigs' snout, the ring then deters the pig from using its snout as a tool to dig up the ground when rooting for food. 19th - 20th Century*

j) Farriers' Searcher *A small horn handled knife, with both curved blade and point. Used by farriers for paring dead material from hooves to make the shoe fit comfortably*

k) Fleam *A veterinary instrument with three sizes of very sharp blades, this was used for bleeding animals with ailments such as high blood pressure. 19th Century*

l) Searing Iron *After heating until red hot in a fire, this tool would have been applied to cauterise and stem blood flow from an animal wound. 19th -20th Century*

m) Balling Gun *For long-necked animals like horses or cattle, this instrument was used to introduce a pelleted ball of medicine down the throat. The trigger releases the pellet well down in the animals' gullet to prevent regurgitation. 19th - 20th Century*

n) Veterinary Syringe *This would have been primarily used for introducing fluids into an animals' rectal orifice*

instruments were used. These included horse tail dockers, a rather crude tool with two handles operating a knife to cut through one of the tail joints, usually close to the rump. Castration clamps or emasculators were applied to young stallions or bulls if the animal was not required for breeding purposes or was needed for beef production. Administration of medicines could be difficult with some animals, and again because a quadruped's body is in the horizontal plane, 'balling' guns were used to deliver pills or other medicinal products, directly into the digestive tract or even the stomach area.

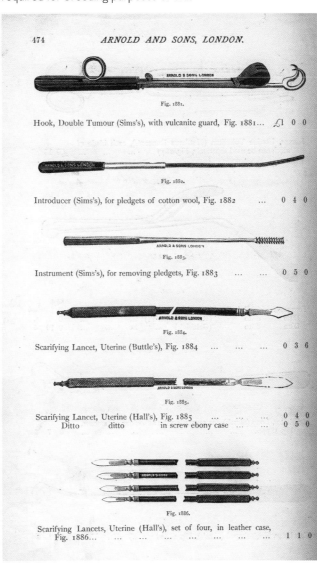

Late 19th Century surgical instruments from Arnold and Sons catalogue

Peter Goss is the last surgical instrument forger left in Sheffield. He can still be seen working at a small forge in Kelham Island Museum, hand forging stainless steel surgical instruments to order, for surgeon's around the world

Between the 19th and 21st Centuries there was a tremendous surge in development and design in many trades, with tools and associated equipment often leading the field but largely unrecognised. Significant advances in Nuclear, Space, Chemical, Aeronautical and Computer technology, have been well documented elsewhere. Here, however, an attempt has been made to highlight one or two of the milestones marking the progress achieved within parts of the tool industry.

Like 'Hoover', the term 'Stanley Knife' has grown into universal usage, and even this humble tool may be found in virtually everyone's toolbox nowadays. The first fixed blade prototype, the 199E was designed by Stanley Works in the USA around 1932 and was used primarily to cut soft-board, a popular building material. The main components were originally cast iron, but later die-cast from a zinc alloy known as 'Mazak', which when locked together with a screw, secured the knife blade. Stanley Works opened a factory in Sheffield in 1937 but it wasn't until 1947 that the Stanley knife came to the UK where it was known as the 'six shilling knife'. By the 1960's Stanley Tools (GB) took up and developed the design and in the 1970's Dick Gilbert was their lead designer, producing many different models up to 1995. The Hawley Collection has many development models, also the original wooden patterns for the 'Titan', one of the last designs, but now with a retractable blade. Other developments in this area included the 'snap off' blade knife which too had many different patterns in both metal and plastic.

The term 'DIY' was coined in the USA around the early 1950's and soon after this, became popular in the UK through a number of TV programmes which promoted home improvement techniques. Developments in measuring equipment such as tapes and rules can be dated back to 1842 when James Chesterman used flat steel strip in relatively short, 6' 0" lengths which were then connected together by means of accurately formed hinge joints to produce long steel tapes. In 1922, Hiram A Farrand in the USA, developed and patented the first convex section steel strips for steel tapes, and this style is still in use today. By 1927 Chesterman had produced the first steel pocket tape measures, later these were enhanced by the addition of DuPont's 'Mylar' coating. Long linen tapes also used extensively for measuring, were inaccurate when wet, and were superseded in the 1950's with the more durable glass-filled nylon tapes made by both John Rabone and James Chesterman, the latter company in fact wove all their own tapes.

Spirit levels were important for many trades but their glass vials were restrictive in use, easily broken or misaligned. In the mid 1950's a 'Monoblock' solid vial was developed. This was made from methyl methacrylate, a clear shatterproof synthetic polymer, sometimes known by the trade names 'Perspex'® and 'Plexiglass'®, the latter patented in Germany in 1933. These vials were produced with an internal barrel shaped form to hold the fluorescent liquid and bubble, and universally used in levels. The German company Stabila, were generally considered as the pioneers in this field.

Wood saws underwent a transformation over a decade starting in 1960 when Brian Asquith did some work for Spear and Jackson and developed a simplified, ergonomically designed handle for their saws. This was followed in 1965 by the introduction of moulded thermoplastic handles and three years later the 'Teflon S'® coating was applied to saw blades under the Black Prince design. In 1970 S & J were producing a range of log saws with induction hardened teeth and this led to the development and introduction of the 'Hardpoint' general purpose wood saw, reported to give four

Fly: *To shear a shape out of flat steel with cutters, or punch out a shape with a machine, known as a Fly Press.*

Turning the hat: *Term used by hand file cutters when working at less than trade prices..*

Wheel swarf: *Sludge formed from the particles of steel and abrasive thrown off the grinding wheel during the grinding of blades.*

13.79

times the life of a standard saw.

Electrically powered tools had been around since the early 1900s but in 1961 Black and Decker produced the first cordless battery-powered drill and in 1969 one was used on the first moon landing by Neil Armstrong. Many developments followed including the introduction of powered hammer drills, sanders, grinders and the like. The first DIY electric drill was the Wolf Cub in 1949 followed by other utility drills made by B & D and Bridges.

Gobbed-on: Soldered on; bolsters, soft-soldered on to pocket knife blades.

Surform was another tool developed in Sheffield around 1949 by Christopher Hodgson Booth at one of the Firth Brown companies who produced a precision engineered tool like a cheese grater with a multitude of blades sharpened to give a shearing action when removing excess material from hardboard, aluminium, copper etc. This was a good DIY tool, made in a variety of patterns for single and two-handed use, round and flat files, planes, shapers etc. and later adapted for electric tools. Stanley Tools bought the USA rights in 1962 when it was first actively marketed by them.

Crappy: Brittle steel, short and crumbly in texture.

Tubular steel handled hammers were developed by Stanley Tools around 1965 due to a shortage of the hickory wood from which they were traditionally made. Later the handles were solid forged, although the USA manufacturer Estwing had used this design for a number of years.

Finally, mention must be made of the Black and Decker 'Workmate'®. This was the first folding portable workbench which reputedly has sold between 50 and 60 million examples worldwide. Originally designed in 1962 by *Ron Hickman, Chief Design Engineer at Lotus Cars, this unique product was covered by twenty patents, but initially no company was really interested in selling it, not even Black & Decker who eventually bought the rights to do so in 1972. There were many attempts by other manufacturers to clone the product, but each design feature was protected by one or more of the patents.

*Ron Hickman, who was known to the author, died on 17th February 2011, as the last pages of this book were being written.

i) **Self Grip Wrench** Originally invented and patented in 1924 by a Mr Petersen in De Witt, Nebraska, USA. Very few were sold in the UK until WW2 when labour was scarce, and it was referred to as a 'third hand'. E Mole and Son, Birmingham, started making these under licence and called it a Mole Wrench, and the name stuck. Mole has now gone but there are many similar copies although the Petersen Company still operates in the USA

j) **Wood Chisels** These tools always suffered abuse from inexperienced operatives, using hammers which broke the wooden handles. Just after WW2, various plastics were developed, which started to be used for handles. This is a range of late 20th Century examples

a) **Electric Power Drill** An early 'portable' tool but heavy and of massive construction; producing a relatively small power output. Used for drilling holes up to ¾" (18mm) in steel. Made in USA c.1900

b) **Electric Drill** The Wolf 'Quartermaster' was designed for the new DIY trade, and advertised as a 'high speed power unit' for powering a variety of attachments to plane, sand and drill wood, brick and steel. Black & Decker and Wolf were early competitors in the fledgling DIY market in the late 1940's and 50's

c) **Tarplaner** This was probably the earliest portable planing machine, produced just after WW2, and was a first class machine. Ken Hawley sold one to a Rotherham Undertaker to plane coffin boards. This is where he noticed an old iron brace on the wall, and acquired it. This was the beginning of the Hawley Collection and the rest is history. c. 1950's

d) **Rawlplug Mechanical Hammer** Instead of producing a hole for a screw using a hammer and wall drill, this tool supposedly made the job easier. The cranked handle was turned, and this rotated the drill, and also 'hammered' at the same time. The strength of the blow was adjusted by means of a screw. In use, it sounded just like a Tommy-gun, and was heavy to carry around in a tool bag. Mid 20th Century

e) **Rawlplug Electric Hammer** This was an early application, using a portable electric power tool for a specific purpose. It was an expensive tool, and not everyone had electric power available where needed! Mid 20th Century

f) **Bolt Cutters** Originally invented in the USA by HK Porter, these were copied, and examples like this were made by C & J Hampton in Sheffield for many years

g) **Hacksaw** This insulated tool made by Sibille was designed to protect power workers from electric shock and 'flashover', and is tested to 1000V. Two special plastic coatings are bonded to the tool which is made from chrome vanadium alloy. The French company makes a wide range of insulated tools for the electrical industry.

h) **Firemans' Axe** Strapped 15" handle and with a chisel pein, this early 19th Century tool was made by Skinner & Johnson, Ranskill, Notts. Marked B.R. 'British Railways', it would have been sited in the guard's van in a passenger train for possible emergencies

a

b

c

d

e

f

g

h

i

j

13.81

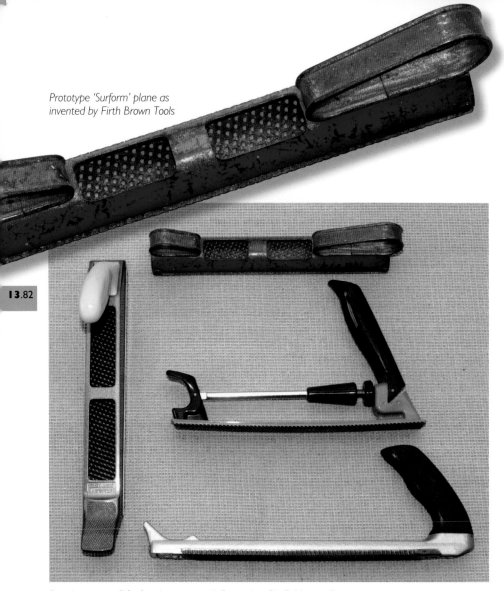

Prototype 'Surform' plane as invented by Firth Brown Tools

13.82

Developments of 'Surform' pattern tools from other Sheffield manufacturers

a) Paramo Plane Master
This woodworking plane from F Parramore & Sons was supplied with a rabetting attachment and throwaway blades. It was the invention of Reg Dakin a Sheffielder, in the 1960's. A world first!

b) Electric Soldering Iron
Previously, soldering irons were heated using external heat in a fire or by means of a blowlamp. Made by Wolf, c.1950's

c) Abrading Tools
The 'Surform' tool inspired competitors to produce similar equivalents without infringing copyright. Here are the Sandvik (orange), and Stanley versions, designed as finishing tools for wood, plastic, leather etc. c.1960's

d), e), f) Multi-blade Tools
Such tools date back to, and were made in Victorian times. However, James Neill introduced their Eclipse 4S diecast tool with different blades in the 1930's (d), mostly for light metalworking etc. During the 1060's Stanley Tools introduced the Stanley replaceable blade knife (see page 84), and many imitations followed. Two multi-blade knives (e) and (f) were made by Steadfast Tools, Sheffield, one with a metal handle, the other with a moulded plastic handle. These were the forerunners of many similar tools to be designed and made in later years. c.1960's

Fetheredged: Having one edge thicker than the other, like an old-fashioned open razor.

a

b

c

d

e

f

13.83

Some familiar, and other unusual 'Stanley' knives made in the period c.1930's to 2000

One of the jewels in the Hawley Collection is the vast resource of library and archive material ranging back into the 18th Century. This is in the process of being catalogued and indexed, but access is already available for students and special research projects. Indeed its reputation is such that enquiries about tools and the old manufacturing methods are regularly received from around the world.

The main subjects covered are hand tools and cutlery worldwide with some 6000 manufacturers' catalogues dating from the early 19th Century, when catalogues were a novelty, right up to the present day when many printed catalogues have been replaced by CD ROM. In addition to the above there are many catalogues from industries including surgical and veterinary, dental instruments, the Sheffield steel industry and even the larger machine tools, some of which were made in the City. Two more unusual industries were those involved in the manufacture of swords and tuning forks, both reliant on special steels.

Some reference has already been made to the Sheffield Illustrated List and these were produced regularly by Pawson and Brailsford and other printers in Sheffield. It had several hundred pages in landscape format containing around 3000 beautiful engravings of products. These Lists are now collectors' items but the Hawley Collection has some thirty different versions ranging from the mid 1800's to early 1900's and the author has regularly referred to these during the production of this book.

The archives contain many handwritten purchase and sales ledgers, Minute books and similar material covering many trades. They are a unique resource giving an insight into the way some of Sheffield's major companies and businesses operated some 100 years or so ago. There are trades union 'Statements,' or price lists for work done over many trades in the tool and

Bolster: *Decorative metal junction between the blade and the tang on table knives; the metal piece attached to the tip of the scales on a folding knife.*

14.85

This 18th Century 45° mahogany instrument, which appears to carry Indian ink stains, is marked out in 5° segments, and there are other linear markings on the angled lines, showing divisions of 1.2 inches. The arm, pivoted on a hand-made brass pin, is fitted with a brass-plated spirit level. To date, a use has not been identified for this item, and suggestions would be welcomed'

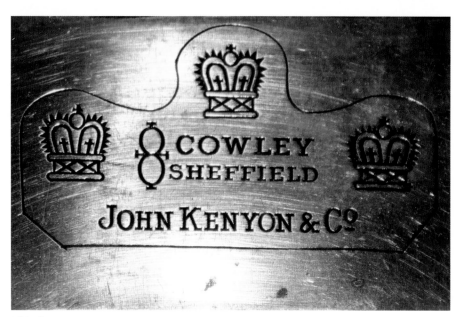

19th Century master plate for acid etching a makers mark on hand or back saw blades

Archive Material

This vast range of tool and cutlery catalogue's, Indentures, Minutes of meetings, original ledgers and workbooks together with photographs, film and video footage, audio tapes and other ephemera, may well be unsurpassed anywhere in the world. It is a massive resource of research material which is continually being accessed by schools, universities and businesses as well as private individuals. At the last count there are more than 10,000 individual items or documents.

The image opposite can only include just a few selected examples, dating from the early 19th Century up to the most recent printed catalogues and brochures. The Hawley Collection covers products from across the world, not just the UK, and is still expanding through gifts and acquisitions, mostly from China and the Far East currently.

Reference is made elsewhere in this publication to the 'Sheffield List', and the Collection owns many examples, in different formats, from c.1850 to 1910. The Sheffield Local History Library also has a number of examples of this publication, which are now quite collectable, particularly by individuals with an interest in tools and their history.

19th Century cutlery catalogues are also very rare, and the Collection is fortunate to own a number of very fine examples, together with some tool, also wood and metalworking machine catalogues. At the bottom of this image, for sheer showmanship, the Austrian scythe list is hard to beat for its colourful display of different scythe patterns, all beautifully illustrated.

cutlery industries. These tell of production processes and types of work from another age, but vital to our understanding of how items were made. The Collection also houses original works drawings of precision measuring tools of world famous companies, now all gone.

For many years in the 20th Century, Light Trades House was the home of the Federation of British Hand Tool Manufacturers, a Trade Association formed to oversee exports, prices and discounts, national and international standards, overseas trade fairs and inward missions from foreign countries. The Association no longer exists but the Hawley Collection now has the only surviving copies of its

Lad: The invariable term for a cutler's 'prentice, hardly ever referred to by name, but as Joby's lad, Billy's lad, etc.

Gassing: 4d. or 6d. a week paid to employers for the use of gas.

Minutes going back many years, dealing with organisation and management of the Sheffield tool-making trades.

Since 1965, Ken Hawley has been taking ciné film and video footage of a number of trades which have now long since disappeared. The last manufacturer of Beech-wood bench, and moulding planes was Wm. Marples in Sheffield and film was taken to show a unique record of this company's manufacturing methods and at the same time, around forty other trades in a number of traditional Sheffield businesses. As far as plane-making was concerned, the complete range of tools for making these planes was acquired and saved for posterity. This is the only

14.87

Archive Material

This image shows a further wide ranging display of sales literature, covering many other areas of the tool and cutlery trades, also wholesalers catalogues, right up to the present day where now, many modern catalogues and price lists are held on CD or DVD's. Buck and Hickman's is just one example, and this old established tool wholesaler operates on a national scale, and imports from the USA and other parts of the world. Even Leicester and Birmingham toolmakers' catalogues are represented here.

Engineers' production drawings too are quite rare and difficult to acquire. However, the Collection has built up a variety of examples from a number of sources, Moore & Wright, James Chesterman, C & J Hampton to name but a few.

Two friends of Ken Hawley had a most unusual 'hobby'. This entailed going into derelict factories and other property after it had been vacated, in order to see what had been left behind! They also removed for 'safekeeping', the signs on the doors! A few of them are shown on the board in the centre of the picture. They represent what Sheffield was, but perhaps not quite as far back as the original 'Little Mesters,' and certainly not what it is like today in the 21st Century

complete collection in the world. In addition, there are many thousands of photographs, engravings and other old illustrations, postcards, etc. showing tool and cutlery manufacture, work in progress together with works interiors going back for 100 years or more. Also in the archive are several thousand printing blocks used in the production of many catalogues and price lists, together with a collection of original drawings and tracings of patterns used by silversmiths from world-famous companies.

All archive material as well as actual tools, and 'work in progress' items, to show how things are made are in frequent use by our research group of dedicated volunteers. They are examining in close detail, joiners planes and plane making, saw manufacture in the golden years 1765 – 1965, and precision measuring tools, where reference can be made to the unique and very large collection of over 300 micrometers. Wire gauges, although now obsolete as a way of measuring thin components is also being extensively researched.

Dialect and trade words are now largely obsolete although they too have been catalogued and introduced as a feature throughout this book, with a glossary at the end. They should not be overlooked as they represent a slice of Sheffield's Light Trades history and tradition, now fast fading into oblivion. The library and archive exists to ensure that not everything is forgotten or lost to future generations.

Race: To pass a sharp metal tool over the face of a spinning grinding wheel in order to remove embedded steel particles, and so 'roughen' the surface; 'racing t'stooan'.

Early 20th Century acid etching plate, used by Sheffield manufacturer Sanderson Brothers and Newbould

Poking: Being forced to take work to another grinding shop, or borrow room to work.

Agon An inverted chisel, fitted cutting edge uppermost in a socket on the forger's anvil to cut off the mood.

Arseboard A board slung from behind the grinder to serve as a seat. It extends forwards between his legs to the wheel. His weight, when sitting on it, converts it into a powerful lever for pressing any objects to be ground, onto the stone.

Ass hoil, ass nook The place under a grate where ashes drop.

Back Spittle A wooden shovel.

Barkle up A verb, to clog up a glazer.

Barmskin A leather apron used by cutlers.

Bellus, or belluses A forger's bellows. Often used in the double plural form.

Benk A bench.

Bitin 'on A snack eaten about eleven in the morning during a short interval from work.

Blank A rough un-worked stamping in metal of any article.

Bosh A vessel containing water for quenching heated blades.

Bolster Decorative metal junction between the blade and the tang on table knives; the metal piece attached to the tip of the scales on a folding knife.

Bows The finger holes in a pair of scissors.

Broddle To enlarge, or ream out a hole, e.g., in a haft or handle, to fit the blade tang.

Buffing Highly polishing a blade on a leather covered wooden wheel. The leather is dressed with emery or other fine abrasive. Leather originally used was buffalo hide, leading to 'buffing'.

Buff stick A flat piece of wood like a leather stick, faced with leather. The article to be polished is rubbed with this.

Bug blinding Lime-washing the workshop, and generally cleaning up.

Bull week The week before Christmas, when the cutlers 'bulled at work', or made an extra effort.

Burnt blades Blades overheated at the wheel which spoils the temper of the steel.

Brat An apron, (pronounced apperon), worn by cutlers.

Candle box A triangular box of wood to shield a candle from the draught in the grinding hull.

Cannelled edge The chamfered edge of a tool, knife or razor when the fetheredge has been removed.

Cap Decorative metal end of carving or table knife handles.

Capping Pinning metal caps on the handle ends.

Chine To cut through anything.

Click howd To catch hold of anything.

Clams Wooden jaws fitted to the steel jaws of a vice, to hold knife handles firmly without damage.

Cloudy A white cloudy patch on the surface of a blade shows a soft part, through a fault either in the steel or in making up.

Clout A cloth used for wiping knives dry and clean.

Clout nail Nail with a large flat head, used for nailing leather on to the wooden drum.

Cog To hammer iron with a power hammer.

Concealed pin Table knives pinned on to the haft from the choil edge (the cutting edge), without carrying the pins right through to the back edge, or 'mock pinned'.

Cotter To strike heavily. "I'll gie thee a good cotter if tha dusn't choil it!"

Crapply Brittle steel, short and crumbly in texture.

Crocus Red iron ore, ground up for use as a polish.

Cuckoos Faulty work, sent back to be put right.

Cutlery Initially, items which 'cut' i.e. table knives (see also flatware).

Cutling Assembling knives.

Datalman, or day-tale man A journeyman, any man paid by the day, and not by piecework rates.

Dead horse Doing work for which the cutler has already subbed, or drawn money in advance.

Devil A piece of flat steel bar, with a slit, cut part way down. This is wedged in a hole in the stiddy, and is used to straighten twisted blades.

Die A steel mould, which when struck, imparts the shape to a blade or some decorative material.

Dish A shallow depression in the scales of a pocket or penknife to make the horn, wood or pearl covering lie flat.

Dollop A lot or large number of articles.

Dolly A log of wood placed in the wet grinder's trough to adjust the level of water to meet the face of the grindstone. Always removed after the days' work, so that the stone is not left in water.

Dolly A wheel of calico discs clamped together, revolving on a glazer's spindle; used for polishing.

Dub A dub point means a rounded end to a blade, like that of an ordinary dinner knife.

Electroplating Electrolytic process of depositing a thin layer of silver onto base metals.

Elsin A shoemaker's awl.

Engraving Incised decoration, using small chisel-like tools, which are sometimes pushed with a wiggling action by the engraver.

Facing Protecting soft iron hammer heads with a hard steel face.

Fairin Small money gifts from workmen and tradesmen to errand lads and warehouse girls at Christmas and Whitsun.

Fash Any rough turned edge caused by filing, or a metal protrusion produced in manufacturing.

Ferrule Decorative metal hoop around a table knife handle, just above or behind the bolster.

Fetheredged Having one edge thicker than the other, like an old-fashioned open razor.

Fey To clean out the sludge or mud from a dam, or grinders trough.

Flat stick Shaped piece of Ash wood, with which the grinder presses the blade to a wheel.

Flatware Forks and spoons which do not cut (see also cutlery.)

Fly To shear a shape out of flat steel with cutters, or punch out a shape with a machine, known as a Fly Press.

Forging Hammering heated steel into shape.

Gaffer A foreman or supervisor.

Gassing 4d. or 6d. a week paid to employers for the use of gas.

Gillies Butcher's knives for the Scottish trade.

Glazer Leather-headed wheel dressed with glue and emery to give finish to blades.

Gobbed-on Soldered on; bolsters, soft-soldered on to pocket knife blades.

Goff hammer Fast-running, powered trip hammer used in forging.

Greasy cutler A hafter; the man who makes, files and fits, bone and horn handles to table cutlery.

Grinding Using an abrasive wheel to put a sharp edge and smooth finish on to a blade.

Grinder's asthma Tuberculosis, caused by breathing in fine dust from stone and metal produced by grinding.

Gullet The hollow between the teeth of a file or saw.

Hack hammer Chisel-faced, adze-shaped hammer used to correct defects in the surface of a grindstone.

Hafting Attaching the handle to a knife or tool.

Hammer plates Thick iron sheets laid on the top of an anvil to protect it from wear.

Heft Or haft to file handles into shape; also, the handle of a knife or blade.

Hottle A covering for a sore finger; also a protective cloth stall to slip over good knife handles.

Housing The framework of a machine.

Jimping A milled, ornamental edge to the liners of a pocket knife; also the decorative grinding on the back of an open razor.

Kelt Money.

Kitt A tub of water, used for washing and cleaning blades, to allow inspection during grinding.

Knifeboard A narrow tray with raised edges for carrying spring knives from shop to factor.

Lad The invariable term for a cutler's 'prentice, hardly ever referred to by name, but as Joby's lad, Billy's lad, etc.

Lap To wrap up any article; also to give a final high finish to a blade.

Latten Thin sheet brass, used for ornamenting knife handles of the cheaper kind.

Lig on To lay on, or put on a great deal of pressure in filing and grinding.

Little mester A master cutler working on his own, but in a rented factory room; he would deal through a factor to sell his goods.

Lood wark Work not completed on time.

Makker A hand forger.

Mark side Side of the blade on which the makers' identifying mark is struck.

Moit A mote in the eye, of steel or stone in particular. Grinders were expert in removing these.

Mood The rough blank or forging of any article. Also used as a verb; to mood, i.e. mould.

Natty money The contribution paid to a Trades' Union or Friendly Society.

Neb The curved tang of a scythe. Neb means any projection, the nose of a man or peak of a cap.

Nickerpecker Nickname for hand file cutters; their hammering was likened to the sound of woodpeckers.

Notch hollow A notch in the scale of a pen or pocket knife, where the thumb goes to reach the nail nick to open the blade.

O-er cutting Most files are double-cut; the o'ercutting is the first cut, and this is crossed by the second 'up' cut.

Outworker A small independent cutler, performing one or two operations in his own home, then returning the article for finishing by others.

Owe To re-surface a grinding wheel, by hacking with a special chisel-edged hammer.

Pane end The opposite end to the face of a hammer head.

Pike The beck, or pointed end of an anvil.

Pile side Reverse side of the blade from the mark side, often shows the cutler's thumb print.

Pistol haft A common type of pocket knife with a haft resembling the butt of an old-fashioned pistol.

Poking Being forced to take work to another grinding shop, or borrow room to work

Prints Pair of dies used to form a table knife bolster.

Putting together Assembling scissors; the 'Scissor Putter Togetherer' is a recognised Sheffield trade.

Quench To temper a heated blade in water or oil.

Race To pass a sharp metal tool over the face of a spinning grinding wheel in order to remove embedded steel particles, and so 'roughen' the surface; 'racing t'stooan'.

Rat-tailed file A 4 or 5 inch slender round file.

Rattening Wilful damage to machinery by strikers.

Reckon To settle up wages.

Rozzil Resin, used for fixing tangs of table knives into the handles.

Sam up Pick up.

Sand rat A moulder.

Saw piercing Decorative fretwork designs made by sawing into spoon tops, fish eaters, bowls, dishes etc.

Scales Two flat pieces of bone, wood etc., riveted to form handles of table, butchers' or folding knives.

Scale tang Tang of a table or butchers' knife, to which two scales are fastened.

Scummer A fire shovel.

Setting Slightly bending and twisting scissor blades so that the edges come together and cut effectively. Bending the teeth of saws so they face alternatively to each side. Both jobs carried out by hammering.

Setting-in Assembling an open razor.

Shank The part of a pair of scissors between the blade and the bow.

Shell Decorative detail on the head of the screw in scissors. Produced by filing a series of lines.

Shut Forge welding a steel face onto wrought iron blades.

Smithing Striking a blade with a chisel-faced hammer to correct any flatness errors caused by the hardening process; hand hammering a machine made spring knife blade.

Snaith The crooked handle of a scythe.

Sours Drawing pay for work not yet done.

Stamping A method of forging hot metal in dies, by means of a heavy, gravity operated weight or tup.

Stiddy Local name for anvils of which there were many patterns made in and used for the Sheffield tool and cutlery trades.

Stock Wooden or stone base for an anvil.

Striker A man wielding a heavy striking hammer to assist the forger in two-handed forging.

Swage Decorative ground bevel, along the back of a knife.

Sweets Goods delivered but not yet paid for.

Tang Metal extension of the bolster to which the table knife or fork handle is attached.

Temper To re-heat steel after hardening and quenching, in order to adjust the precise degree of hardness to the metal.

Thumb mark A patch or mark on the pile (reverse), side of a table knife blade, where the iron tang and bolster iron has been welded to the shear steel blade.

Tines Prongs or points of any instrument.

Tilt A forge, power hammer, originally worked by water power, sometimes called a 'trip hammer'.

Trow A water trough, in which the wet grinding wheels run.

Turning the hat Term used by hand file cutters when working at less than trade prices.

Upglazing Buffing a blade on a wooden wheel, dressed with glue and emery, to remove scratches and give a fine black finish.

Wasters Imperfect articles, throwouts.

Walk and talk Phrase describing the smooth opening and closing action of a spring knife.

Wheel Term used to describe a grindstone.

Wheel A building to house several grinding wheels, powered by water, later by steam or electricity.

Whet To sharpen knives or tools.

Whetstone A slab of Brincliffe stone. Warehouse women used to swish the knife edge quickly along the stone to produce a keen cutting edge.

Wheel swarf Sludge formed from the particles of steel and abrasive thrown off the grinding wheel during the grinding of blades.

Whittle An early knife, carried in a sheath on the person and used as a general purpose knife.

Wimble A boring tool.

Witch A tool used by spring knife cutlers to stop scales bending, whilst being riveted.

Xylonite An early form of plastic, used for knife handles.

Yarmouth beef Or two-eyed beef steak (red herrings); the only beef a poor cutler could afford.

Yaller belly A grinder's nickname, owing to the yellow swarf he was covered with from his wheel.

BIBLIOGRAPHY AND FURTHER READING

Barnes, Janet, (1992) *The Cutting Edge, Catalogue for an Exhibition of Sheffield Tools, Sheffield,* The Ruskin Gallery

Dyson, B. Ronald, (1936, Reprinted 1979), *A Glossary of Words and Dialect, Formerly used in The Sheffield Trades,* Sheffield, University of Sheffield Printing Unit

Rolt, L.T.C. (1965), *Tools for the Job, A Short History of Machine Tools,* London, B.T.Batsford

Rowe, Robert, (Ed) (1998), *The Toolbank Collection,* London, Scorpion Cavendish Ltd.

Sheffield Illustrated List, *(Various editions),* Sheffield, Pawson & Brailsford

Unwin, Joan and Hawley, Ken, (1999), *Sheffield Industries' Cutlery, Silver and Edge Tools,* Stroud, Tempus Publishing

Unwin, Joan and Hawley, Ken, (2003), *A Cut above the Rest, The Heritage of Sheffield's Blade Manufacture,* Sheffield, The Hawley Collection Trust